The Golden Age of
Quaker Botanists

Ann Nichols

Ann Nichols

The Quaker
Tapestry
Kendal in Cumbria

To my husband, Harold, who died before I
could put this book into his hands. We enjoyed
many discussions and friendly
arguments as we researched together.
His commitment to the Quaker Tapestry
Scheme over twenty years is completed in
this book.

ISBN 0 9525433 7 0

Designed by Jeremy Greenwood, Woodbridge
and printed by Middleton's Print Works,
Ambleside, Cumbria LA22 9DJ

for the Quaker Tapestry at Kendal
Friends Meeting House
Stramongate
Kendal, Cumbria
LA9 4BH

the permanent home of the
Quaker Tapestry Collection

frontispiece
Armeria maritima
Anne Dent

Table of contents

ACKNOWLEDGMENTS

My love and gratitude to my husband, Harold Nichols, who first suggested this book, and then enthusiastically undertook much of the research, giving me confidence, support and wise advice.

The editing has been a revelation! Ros Morley has led me gently but firmly towards a more cohesive and readable book, unstinting in her interest and efforts.

Jeremy Greenwood, designer and publisher, has given so much time, thought and expertise to this book that the original manuscript has been transformed.

I have been astonished and grateful for the help, support and encouragement from those connected with the Quaker Tapestry; Bridget Guest and the Publications Committee of the Quaker Tapestry, and those many friends who made valuable comments on the manuscript.

To my family who were in no doubt that a book would finally emerge; to my grandson Simon Clint who passed on his computer, and to his parents John and Gail and his sister Sarah, who patiently taught me how to use it and were always so willing to come to my rescue.

One small book, so much goodwill and encouragement in the generous spirit of the Tapestry Scheme. I am truly grateful.

In 1987 Radio 4 broadcast a series that traced the growth of gardens from the old monastery herb garden to the present day. During one programme, which was mainly about Quaker plant hunters, the presenter said that probably a thousand plants in our gardens were introduced or raised by Quakers in the late seventeenth century through to the nineteenth century. Intrigued by this, I mentioned it to Anne Wynn-Wilson, the founder of the Quaker Tapestry, a project my husband Harold and I were heavily involved with at that time; Harold was a researcher and I was part of the teaching and production group. From its quiet beginnings as a project for a Children's Meeting in Taunton, the idea of a tapestry depicting Quaker personalities, Quaker thought and Quaker activities throughout the 300 years of its history captured the imagination, not just of the children, but of Quakers world-wide.

It so happened that Anne had been considering a panel that would be embroidered entirely by the teachers. We had taught at workshops, advised many groups and overseen so many panels (in my case twenty-seven) that she thought we would enjoy one of our own! A panel on Quaker botanists and plant hunters would be ideal, because to embroider flowers, using only the five stitches which are used on the Quaker Tapestry panels, would take all our ingenuity and creativity. Almost immediately, she began sketching out a design.

Harold and I started the research, visiting the Lindley (Royal Horticultural Society) Library, the Chelsea Physic Garden, Friends House Library, and others. Fortunately we then lived in Wokingham and could travel easily and cheaply to London, and Kew Gardens was also on our train line. All Anne asked from us was a list of plant hunters, botanists, plant collectors, horticulturists, nurserymen and about twenty flowers from which she could choose and so our research at that time was not very wide or deep. It was, however, enough to spark our interest and for us to say, 'One day, we'll really explore this subject!'

By 1996, when the Tapestry Exhibition was established at Kendal in Cumbria, there was

more time for us to start thinking about it. Harold again did most of the research, and we were lent notes made by Fred Fletcher (member of the Quaker Meeting in Hull, researcher, speaker, and for many years the knowledgeable head gardener at Hull University). These notes were an excellent verification of our own findings.

It soon became obvious that for two and a half centuries there had been a disproportionate number of Quakers at the forefront of science. Consider just a few of the Quaker scientists who made new discoveries and advances in their field – Doctors John Fothergill, John Coakley Lettsom, and Joseph Lister; John Dalton; and the Darby family, the ironmasters at Coalbrookdale. Later we see Arthur Stanley Eddington and Kathleen Lonsdale – the list is long.

Why was this the case, we wonder? Part of the answer for the earlier scientists must lie, strangely enough, in the somewhat narrow views that many Quakers held at that time. Music, painting, sculpture, dance and the theatre were not encouraged; we should not try to copy the perfection of God's natural world,

QUAKER BOTANISTS panel D8 of the Quaker Tapestry

7

maybe? The quilts made by the Amish community always contain at least one mistake, because only God is perfect. But this could only be a small part of the answer; the rest lies in the nature of Quakerism itself.

The Quaker book of discipline – *Quaker faith & practice* (1994) – has this passage by Charles Carter, sometime vice-chancellor of Lancaster University: 'True faith is not assurance, but the readiness to go forward experimentally, without assurance. It is a sensitivity to things not yet known. Quakerism should not claim to be a religion of certainty, but a religion of uncertainty; it is this which gives us our special affinity to the world of science.' (26.39, 1971)

George Fox (1624-1691), the founder of Quakerism, encouraged science and research. Quakers had a relatively radical approach to education and about what education should be – which was not the narrow classicism of the old universities. As a result, there was a great burgeoning of questioning and first-hand research.

One of the first educationalists and botanists, Thomas Lawson, a personal friend of George Fox, believed that education should teach us more about the world in which we live: 'Children and Youth read the Natures of Trees, Birds, Beasts, Fish, Serpents, Insects, Earths, Metals, Salts, Stones ... also rules for Gardening, Agriculture, Grazing of Cattel, Buildings, Navigation, Arithmatick, Geography, Chronology, sound History, Medicine, knowledge in Law, Improvement of Lands, Chirurgery, Traffick Government, ordering of Bees, Propagation of Plants by Roots, Seeds, Slips, Layers, Suckers by Grafting, Inoculating, Imping, and of Geometry.' (Dagon's Fall 1679:86–7, in Whittaker 1986:123) And we think the National Curriculum is overloaded! You may have noticed, however, that there is no mention of any form of the Arts.

And yet, and yet . . , these Quakers appreciated the beauty and form of a flower, the colours and formation of rocks, the intricacies of a butterfly's wing, the symmetry and grace of a skein of geese flying in formation. It was an intriguing background to the research and, I believe, made us aware of elements, other than the purely scientific, which made these Quakers 'tick'.

It was not only the Quakers, of course. This same explosion and excitement as new discoveries were made and horizons grew wider consumed the whole of the scientific world and instigated friendships and exchanges across the spectrum. The eighteenth century saw the foundation of many learned societies and institutions: The Royal Society of Edinburgh (1731), The Royal Society of Arts (1754), The Linnaean Society (1788), The Royal Institute (1799), and early into the next century The Geographical Society of London (1807) and The Royal Geographical Society (1836).

This same period saw the opening of the Royal Botanic Gardens at Kew, the Chelsea Physick Garden and the Westminster Garden, and we note the flourishing of the private gardens of John Fothergill, Peter Collinson, and John Coakley Lettsom, whilst the influx of new plants led to a renewed interest in the gardens and estates of Lord Petre and the Dukes of Norfolk, Richmond and Bedford. We shall read more of these characters and gardens in the following chapters, as well as of the nurseries which sprang up all over London and further afield, headed by knowledgeable and enthusiastic gardeners.

Two questions that we could not resolve satisfactorily were 'Who should receive the credit for introducing a particular plant?' and 'Could we be accurate about the dating of these introductions?' These two considerations alone make for imprecision, despite considerable research. There was real co-operation between the botanists, plant hunters, collectors, nurserymen and gardeners as they were all caught up in the excitement – but to whom should we give the credit for the introduction of some new flower or plant?

The *botanists* had a great need to know and understand the world of plants and most readily embraced the Linnaean classification when it was introduced. They were the ones who identified the finds and could often say whether this was indeed a species new to them. But should the credit be given to the *plant hunters*, who in addition to a spirit of adventure and ability to conquer the vagaries of climate, the dangers, and often the loneliness, had also to have a good working knowledge of botany? Should it go to the *collectors* who wanted the discoveries in their own gardens, national collections, or parks? These were the people who commissioned the plant hunters, received their seeds and plants in varying states of growth, who propagated, identified, and then opened their gardens to other horticulturists and enthusiasts. Or maybe the credit should go to the *nurserymen* and *gardeners* who took seeds of doubtful viability and coaxed and nurtured them into life, or grew plants from unprepossessing and pitiful beginnings, studying soil and climatic conditions as they learned. Botanists, plant hunters, collectors, nurserymen and gardeners, all co-operated to add to the pool of knowledge and to our heritage of garden plants and trees from all over the world.

The second question concerned the dating of the introductions. Often the first introduction died out, was later re-introduced and survived. How can we date a seed which could produce an annual flower, a bulb or a tree? Do we wait for the flowering as confirmation? This could take many years. Or should it be counted from the time it was planted and began its life? Meanwhile, a plant hunter has sent a specimen almost in bloom.

And so we find conflicting dates and introductions incorrectly credited. Carl von Linné (1707–1778) and Philip Miller (Chelsea Gardener 1691–1771) often claimed credit for plants when that credit should have gone to others. We have done our best to be accurate but not obsessively so. The introduction of so many new plants and the fascinating lives of the people involved is, we believe, a more discernible consideration.

Where and when did it all start? The first recorded plant-hunting expedition was that of Queen Hatshepsut of Egypt, who, *c.*1490 B.C., sent five ships to the Land of Punt to fetch back seeds, plants and trees for her garden. The main quarry was frankincense, a tree gum. A wall carving at Karnak records that thirty-one such trees were established in the Queen's garden.

Gardeners have been with us since man first scratched at the soil and covered seeds. Nurserymen evolved when the gardeners grew an excess of plants for their own use and sold or bartered the surplus. Botany was important to distinguish the beneficial herbs from the poisonous plants, and botanical drawings conveyed that information more widely. The monastery gardens – monasteries were then the main hostelries for travellers – are themselves a source of great interest as they provided food, which involved growing herbs for the pot – borage, mints, parsley, sage, chicory and mustard. For the brewing of ale they grew wormwood and southernwood; and whilst lavender would ward off lice, flax could be woven into linen for the rich travellers.

One of the duties of the monks was the care of the sick and wounded. The herb comfrey is also called knitbone and was used in poultices; there was coltsfoot for coughs and scabious for the itch; feverfew reduced temperature and cured headaches, whilst a brew from the belladonna and the opium poppy would give a few hours relief from pain – although sometimes longer relief in the form of death. After the Dissolution of the Monasteries (1536–40) the knowledge gained by the monks was taken over by the apothecaries and was the standard training for physicians until the two disciplines started to separate in the late seventeenth century.

The *Herball or Generall Historie of Plantes* (1597) by John Gerard (1545–1612) is one of the earliest plant catalogues and marks the beginning of the age of plant collecting and plant hunting. His was the earliest truly botanic garden in this country, followed by that of John Parkinson (1567–1650) and of the Tradescants, father and son plant hunters (c.1570–1638 and 1608–62). Up to this period there had been an emphasis on plants which were useful for food, for flavourings, for medicines and for perfumery rather than for purely decorative or ornamental purposes, but botanists were now looking at the structure of plants, recording them in detail and making drawings.

John Parkinson was apothecary to James I and King's Botanist to Charles I. His book, *Paradisi in sole: Paradisus terrestris, or A garden of all sorts of pleasant flowers which our English Ayre will permit to be noursed up* (1629) was a herbal and an early gardening manual. The Latin title is a pun on his name, meaning 'The earthly paradise of Park-in-sun'. Gerard's *Herball* is sometimes also a commentary on contemporary life and thought: 'The root of Solomons Seale stamped whilst it is fresh and greene, and applied, taketh away in one night, or two at the most, any bruise, blacke or blew spots gotten by falls or women of wilfulnesse, in stumbling vpon their hasty husbands fists, or such like.' (Gerard: 1633:906)

It is about this time that we first find the word 'florist', which originally described the nurserymen who raised flowers. The monks had also grown flowers for church celebrations and marriage ceremonies – roses, lilies, and pinks – and from Edmund Spenser's poems we read of pawnce (pansy), daffadowndillies, gillyflowers (dianthus), coronations (large pinks) and Dame's violets.

The great plant hunters the Tradescants were on the scene in the early seventeenth century, travelling in Russia and Spain. Some of the flowers we plant today, however, are comparative latecomers – *Anemone blanda* and the bright yellow *Genista lydia*, for example, being introduced during the twentieth century.

So the Quakers were late on the scene – but they soon made up for lost time!

Early botanists and illustrators

SCHOOLMASTER AND EXPERT BOTANIST

In the summer of 1652 in the village of Rampside near Ulverston the minister, a young man of 22, had agreed to allow the travelling preacher George Fox to speak to his congregation. As we read in Fox's *Journal* the minister 'very lovingly spoke in the morning to his people of my coming in the afternoon, and when I was come all the country gathered thereaways' (Nickalls, 1975:115) and in order to ensure the safety of the visiting preacher he walked a mile or more to meet him and bring him into the village. THOMAS LAWSON (1630–91) was the name of the young priest who offered his pulpit to the itinerant preacher. It was, however, refused by George Fox who preferred instead to stand on a wooden bench to speak. Thomas Lawson was convinced of the truth of the Quaker message that day and joined the growing numbers of people later to be known as Quakers.

Thomas Lawson was born at Lawkland, a parish of Clapham in the Yorkshire Dales. In 1642, the year in which the Civil War began, Thomas was walking more than two miles every morning over the escarpment to Giggleswick School to begin lessons at 6.30. He learnt Greek, Hebrew and Latin and, we believe, was awarded a scholarship to Christ's College, Cambridge. This scholarship, worth a meagre £5 yearly, did not provide Thomas with sufficient funds so he entered as a sizar – a student who was given tuition and lodging and who in return acted as a servant to a richer student.

Oliver Cromwell was now Head of State following the turbulent years of the Civil War. Cambridge University was part of the ferment which did not cease with the ending of hostilities. The year before Thomas Lawson entered Christ's College William Dell, a radical educational reformer, was made Master of Caius. Dell wanted to see a university curriculum based less upon heathen classics and more upon the Christian tradition and current thinking and experience. Politically

this would help to break the tradition that only gentlemen with a grounding in the classics could enter the universities, which had inevitably led to a virtual monopoly of posts in medicine, law and the church. Thomas Lawson must have been caught up in this new thinking, as is evident in his later writings, and it is possibly this disaffection, as much as lack of money, which led him to leave Cambridge less than two years after entering, without a degree but with his ideas on radical education beginning to crystallise.

Thomas Lawson then went north, bound for the small coastal village of Rampside, four miles south of Barrow-in-Furness. We can only surmise that he knew of the opening for a minister in this village through his old friends at Giggleswick School, or through correspondence between his home in Lawkland and Cambridge University. He travelled north through a country ravaged by war – a country materially and spiritually in turmoil, impoverished, with beggars at every turn and prisons full of debtors – honest men in misery and bewilderment at their changed lives, their destitute families in confusion and despair.

It was a lengthy journey that Thomas Lawson undertook, largely on foot with perhaps occasional lifts from passing wagons, travelling northwards, then possibly turning west over the head of Morecambe Bay. Did Thomas Lawson travel this lengthy route or, as many seventeenth-century travellers preferred, cut across the sands of Morecambe Bay? This would save over sixteen miles, a day's journey, but was a passage made hazardous by quicksand, tides and shifting channels. In spite of the dangers, this route was well used by carts and coaches, sheep and cattle, as well as by riders on horseback and by walkers.

With certainty we know that later in his botanical diaries Thomas Lawson records sea-lavender (*Limonium vulgare*, opposite) and thrift (*Armeria maritima*, frontispiece) as growing on Harlsyde (now Chapel Island), an island in the middle of the estuary which provided refuge for those travellers finding themselves in difficulty.

And so to the village of Rampside, a village

opposite
Limonium vulgare
Anne Dent

in need of a priest, where Thomas Lawson became vicar, although he was not ordained as such. Being well educated, he set up a school there and, as we know, he welcomed the travelling preacher George Fox – an event that changed his life.

Near Ulverston, not far from Rampside, was Swarthmoor Hall. This was the home of Margaret Fell (now affectionately known as the mother of Quakerism). The Hall became a powerhouse – the administrative and spiritual centre of the Quaker movement under the skilled and practical organisation of Margaret Fell. From Swarthmoor Hall were sent the Valiant Sixty, travelling preachers who took the Quaker message to all parts of the country and abroad. Thomas Lawson became one of this band of men and women who were reviled, persecuted and imprisoned and yet who remained steadfast in their faith and in their radical message.

Thomas Lawson's first *Quaker* ministry as a travelling preacher was to his own village of Lawkland, in the Dales where he was born. This must have been difficult, for in an account of his visit entitled 'A paper given forth by Tho. Lawson' [relating to his visit to Lawkland] he writes that when he started to speak his adversaries were 'raising filthy lies, slaunders, aspersions against me, speaking many filthy things of me' (*c.*1653). He was physically assaulted in the churchyard by the infuriated villagers, whilst in the church itself the vicar actually gave Thomas Lawson a hefty punch which knocked him over the pews. He was then beaten over the head with bibles wielded by some of the congregation. His preaching probably had little effect on this occasion!

Travelling in the ministry is a phrase used by Quakers to describe the activities of the men and women who journeyed far and wide in this country and abroad, often meeting physical abuse, to spread the message of Quakerism and to encourage the small groups of Quakers.

Continuing east towards York Thomas Lawson had his first experience of imprisonment, in York Castle. In the spring of 1655 he turned south to Sussex and Surrey, visiting Quakers in London, and returned north about six months later to write pamphlets, booklets and letters. He was a frequent visitor at Swarthmoor Hall where he met with many other travelling Quakers, sharing experiences, and where he was much valued as an administrator by Margaret Fell. We know that he used his knowledge of Hebrew to study original texts of the Bible. In 1659 he married Frances Wilkinson of Great Strickland and became a farmer, continuing his

writing and setting up a school in his own house, although his licence to teach had been revoked. He was a gifted teacher and his school prospered, even though he was often in trouble with the authorities and was continually in court for non-payment of tithes and for attending Quaker Meetings instead of the established Church. The authorities finally closed his school in 1674.

It was then that Thomas Lower, son-in-law to Margaret Fell, employed Thomas Lawson as a tutor to teach him and the daughters of Margaret Fell 'the knowledge of herbs' (Penney, 1920:95). This is the first indication of Thomas Lawson's love of botany and passion for plants. Thomas Lower was a physician and we can suppose, therefore, that the knowledge that he sought was wider than the identification and use of medicinal herbs.

The first botanical records made by Thomas Lawson were almost entirely local. He lists crowberries (*Empetrum nigrum*) in the woods of Whinfell, hedge mustard (*Sisymbrium officinale*) and the delicate maiden pink (*Dianthus deltoides* – opposite) growing behind the parsonage at Cliburn and at Lowther. Whilst visiting the ruins of Furness Abbey he records finding pellitory-of-the-wall (*Parietaria judaica*), the monks' remedy for kidney stones and bladder problems. Here he also found deadly nightshade (*Atropa belladonna*), useful for deadening pain but fatal if used injudiciously. This plant was to be found on the official seal of Furness Abbey and was later to be painted on the carriage doors of the trains run by the Furness Railway Company.

Probably the most eminent botanist at this time and a contemporary of Thomas Lawson was John Ray. The two men corresponded and exchanged plants. John Ray recorded many of Lawson's discoveries in his county catalogues of plants, meticulously attributing them to the Cumberland botanist. Thomas Lawson continued travelling in the ministry, combining with this the botanical recording of plants found on his travels.

In 1677 we can see the guiding hand of George Fox and Margaret Fell when the botanist undertook the long journey to London. Thomas Lawson probably carried with him his essay *Baptismalogia, or a treatise concerning Baptisms: whereto is added a Discourse concerning the Supper, Bread and Wine; Called also Communion* (1677/8) which was published in London some months after his arrival. Knowing the great interest that George Fox had in botany, we can assume Fox suggested that Thomas Lawson should combine his botanical observations and

opposite
Dianthus deltoides
Anne Dent

recording with travelling in the ministry, visiting groups of Quakers and helping them in any way he could as well as by preaching and by intercession on their behalf with the authorities.

We know he did this in Lancashire. Sir Ralph Ashton of Whalley Hall is recorded many times in the records of Lancaster Quarterly Meeting as being tireless in his efforts to force Quakers to pay tithes, sending in bailiffs to seize their property or to have them imprisoned. However, Thomas Lawson seems to have been something of a diplomat for he records lamb's lettuce (*Valerianella locusta*) on a walk with Sir Ralph round his garden, indicating that the meeting was friendly.

Sometimes Thomas Lawson would simply share his knowledge of Quaker events coming, as he did, directly from Swarthmoor Hall and having gathered news as he travelled. His notebook includes a plan showing his itinerary (complete with mileage), events and people (recorded somewhat haphazardly), but his plant observations are meticulous in their accuracy. Where he has any doubts he appears to have consulted other botanists and books as he travelled.

Thomas Lawson was one of the earliest botanists to realise the importance of recording plant distribution. He began with his early local accounts, gathering new knowledge on his journeying – the whole countryside was full of plants he had heard of but wanted to see and document himself.

Botany was interspersed with meeting Quakers persecuted for their beliefs, and he was saddened and indignant at the treatment of Quakers in Gloucester, largely because of the vindictiveness of one Justice Meredith, who actually undertook the whipping of two Quakers himself and had two of his own men beaten because they were not sufficiently enthusiastic in their brutal terrorism of Quakers. Thomas Lawson writes that, in the opinion of the magistrates there, 'it was no more sin to kill a Quaker than to kill a dog' (Besse, 1753:1.219). At the same time, he records that the pea-like flowers of the restharrow (*Ononis spinosa*) were in bloom. This plant, with its tough rootstock, was a menace to farmers, its presence in pasture usually indicating poor cultivation.

London was a delight to Thomas Lawson – he saw the growing interest and enthusiasm for plants which resulted in the increasing number of gardens and herbaria, and he found many to share his own passion. There was a stirring throughout the whole of educated society for a new outlook on science, based on observations and experiment rather than received wisdom

and theory. He found that he had much in common with men of different religious persuasions – Catholics, Anglicans, Presbyterians and Atheists. In 1677 he doubtless saw the newly erected Monument in Fish Street recording the Great Fire of 1666 which had swept away nearly all of the city as he had seen it on his first visit. He records the plants found on the waste ground that sprang up after the fire, much as were seen on the bombsites in the Second World War. He lists Roman chamomile (*Chamaemelum nobile*), buckshorn plantain (*Plantago coronopus*) and many others – although not the flower we associate with the aftermath of the Blitz, the rosebay willow herb (*Chamaenerion angustifolium*) which was a rare plant at this time. Instead he noted the vigorous London rocket (*Sisymbrium irio*).

Thomas Lawson visited many of the gardens, herbaria and plant collections that were appearing around the City, and we can imagine his excitement as he sees and records many of the new plants from all parts of the world. The Westminster Garden near the Abbey had its beginnings around 1650 and was the most important garden at that time – although the Chelsea Physick Garden, still in its infancy, would later come into greater prominence. Thomas Lawson wrote about four separate visits to the Westminster Garden and records almost 500 different plants. His list is the most comprehensive available although it contains only about one third of the plants there.

Having witnessed the publication of his treatise and attended many of the Quaker meetings in London Thomas Lawson turned northward again. His head must have been filled with the delights of the many plants he had seen, new introductions as well as native species. He travelled through Cambridgeshire, where John Ray, a seventeenth-century English clergyman and author had published the very first county flora, *Catalogus Plantarum circa Cantabrigiam nascentium* (Flora of Cambridgeshire), and the only reference book which Thomas Lawson carried with him, *Catalogus Plantarum Angliae*. No doubt it was with great pleasure that he followed the steps of John Ray and noted for himself the flowers and plants that Ray had seen. He discovered only one rarity on this occasion, a white-flowered rock rose.

Thomas Lawson did not compile a county flora as such, although his note book, as well as commenting on the importance of plant distribution (a fact not widely recognised until then) concentrates on the plants of Lancashire and Westmorland. According to William

Nicolson marginal notes were made in Thomas Lawson's copy of Ray's *Catalogus Plantarum Angliae*. William Nicolson was an eminent Church of England cleric, an Archdeacon when he met Thomas Lawson in about 1690. In spite of their very different religious persuasions the two became great friends because of their shared interest in botany. They spent several holidays together, studying and recording plants in their habitat. Nicolson was meticulous about documenting Thomas Lawson's botanical discoveries, putting the letters T.L. against these findings. These were recorded in 'Flora' (this may be a shortened name for *A Seventeenth Century Flora of Cumbria, William Nicolson's catalogue of plants*, 1690).

Thomas Lawson's faith and beliefs were inseparable from his love of plants, for he saw God in all living things and delighted in their beauty, arrangement and complexities. Too early to embrace the Linnaean classification of plants, the nomenclature he uses is lengthy and cumbersome and sometimes makes modern identification more difficult. For example Thomas Lawson records one of the saxifrages in Westmorland as *Saxifrage graminea pusilla folliis brevioribus crassioribus et succulentioribus*, a description of the plant in Latin (in English: tiny, grassy saxifrage with rather short, rather thick and rather succulent leaves).

Many of the later Quaker botanists supported Carl von Linné, known as Linnaeus, a Swedish botanist who introduced a much simpler system. It was binomial, consisting basically of two names for each plant name; the first denoting the genus, a group of closely related species within a family of plants, the second name denoting the species or particular member of that genus. The classification was based upon the reproductive parts of the plant.

Many Quaker botanists were amongst the scientists who set up the Linnaean Society of London in 1788, ten years after the death of Linnaeus. Thomas Lawson's notebooks are now in the care of that Society with microfiche in Durham University.

Thomas Lawson had strong radical ideas, as did most Quakers of that time, about what true education should be. The Universities of Oxford and Cambridge would not accept Dissenters and continued to teach a curriculum of classicism and narrow theology that was an unhelpful preparation for the coming commercial and industrial society. The attitude of Quakers towards the conventional university education of the time doubtless accounts for the numbers of Quakers enquiring into science and the natural world, seeking basic truths for themselves through experimentation. Then, in the next century, they applied their findings to the world of invention, commerce and industry.

In 1690, the year before he died, Thomas Lawson revived the idea suggested by George Fox and William Penn for the setting up of a Garden School to teach botany and horticulture. He wrote to John Rodes, a Derbyshire Quaker, advocating such a venture and offering himself as Master, thus hoping to bring together the two main strands of his life, teaching and botany, both in perfect harmony with his religious beliefs. However he died before anything came of his idea and he is buried at Newby Head in Cumbria, in a small burial ground. There are now only four gravestones there, the one marking Thomas Lawson and his wife Frances standing higher than the other three, which is most unusual for a Quaker headstone. It is said that it was erected by some of his pupils and reads: 'In the tomb below lies the body of Thomas Lawson of Great Strickland, Schoolmaster and expert botanist who died 12th November 1691 aged 61'.

WILLIAM CURTIS AND HIS KIN

Two lads lay in the field, listening to the incessant hum of insects, their noses tickled by the long grasses, and watching the skylark ascending higher and higher until it was lost against the sky. But this was no aimless whiling away of a sunny afternoon – each of the boys carried a book, a magnifying glass, a notebook, some glass phials and a knife. They were already keen naturalists and budding botanists, and the books they carried were the Gerard and Parkinson herbals, books well respected in their time but their information, with superstition and quackery alongside sometimes suspect botany, was being questioned by the more discerning reader, and, already, WILLIAM CURTIS (1746–99) was a sceptic and critic.

He studied any books on the subjects dear to his heart – birds (their eggs and their songs), insects, and especially plants. He and Thomas Legg bent low over a bush, coaxing an unidentified insect into one of the glass phials that William Curtis had begged from his grandfather, the Alton village surgeon-apothecary. Thomas Legg, who had a flair for natural history, was an ostler at the Crown Inn, next door to the apothecary's shop: 'He was not a man of much education, but possessed enough to absorb information from the herbals of Parkinson and Gerard. This he had done to such purpose that … there were few wild plants in the district that he could not name.' (Field and Semple, 1878:104.) The two companions roamed the countryside, laying the foundation for William Curtis to become one of the country's foremost botanists.

William Curtis was born in Alton into a Quaker family, the son of a tanner who was able to ensure that William was well educated. He attended a Friends (Quaker) school in Burford, before becoming apprenticed to his grandfather. Eventually he moved to London where he was apprenticed to the apothecary George Vaux with a view to becoming a doctor, and shortly afterwards to Thomas Talwyn of Gracechurch Street. Talwyn, having no son of his own and being fond of his hard-working and keen apprentice, left his practice to William Curtis. But William's heart was in botany, preferring plants and animals to medicine, and after a few years he sold the practice. He continued to live at No. 51 Gracechurch Street, however, while at No. 40 there lodged a Dr Coakley Lettsom (see p.36). Together with Dr John Fothergill (see p.30), they shared many common interests, as well as their Quakerism, and this led to many years of fruitful friendship.

One First Day (Quaker term for Sunday) in 1770, after Meeting for Worship, a small group of Quakers made their way up Gracechurch Street to have lunch with William Curtis and his wife. John Fothergill and his sister Ann, along with John Coakley Lettsom and his wife (also called Ann), had been invited to hear an exciting proposal which William Curtis hoped to discuss with his friends. After lunch the three men went into the study and we can imagine that it was with some excitement that he told of his proposal to buy a small piece of land in Bermondsey and to start a botanical garden there.

As new and exciting plants had been brought into gardens from many parts of the world, William Curtis felt that the native plants were being sadly neglected. He envisaged a teaching garden, a large proportion of which would be given to the growing and labelling of indigenous plants – or those which had been in this country for so long that they were thought of as native. Each plant was to be classified according to the new Linnaean system. As the friends talked, it became clear that William had thought through his proposals – the educational and financial aspects as well as the purely horticultural implications.

And so, with help and encouragement from many quarters, William Curtis began the task of designing and planting a botanical garden which opened in 1772. Later that year, he was given the post of Demonstrator of Botany to the Society of Apothecaries, and remained in that post for five years.

During this time he started to compile *Flora Londinensis*. It appeared in folio size (slightly smaller than the modern A1 paper size), each issue to contain six plates and accompanying text, covering eventually all the plants to be found within a ten-mile radius of London. The plates were accurately drawn and hand-coloured by eminent artists, including James Sowerby and Sydenham Edwards, and each issue was sold at five guineas a copy. Interestingly, the text contains comments with which we can empathise today: 'The rage for building joined with the ruinous alterations perpetually making in the environs of London, have been the means of extirpating many plants.' He goes on to list the many plants lost in this way.

Flora Londinensis brought him recognition and acclaim but, as William Curtis himself says, 'no pudding'. It was not a financial success and was discontinued through lack of subscriptions. Nevertheless he continued to write. He was intensely interested and knowledgeable about insects and after publishing a book on the subject, he translated and illustrated a book on insects written by Linnaeus.

In 1778 he published his *Proposals for opening the London Botanic Garden*. The garden was to be opened on the first day of January 1779. The three Quaker doctors, John Fothergill, John Coakley Lettsom and William Curtis, together with the nurseryman James Lee, were all by this date committed to spreading the knowledge of the Linnaean classification. They had met and talked with Linnaeus, listened to his lectures, read his books and papers and spoken to the Royal Society on his work. When Linnaeus died in 1778 they began with others to form the Linnaean Society in London which was eventually founded ten years later.

1778 was a busy year for William Curtis. Not only was he involved with the formation of the Linnaean Society but also in moving plants from Bermondsey to the new site on St George's Fields through Lambeth Marsh village: 'Its situation being low, renders it particularly favourable to the growth of aquatic and bog plants, and all such as love a moist bottom, an inestimable advantage in dry summers.' (Curtis, 1783)

He published a catalogue, in which he recorded his thanks to William Aiton, the director of Kew Gardens, for the gifts of many valuable plants. The list of herbs he divided into mediaeval, culinary, poisonous, and medicinal; he listed their periods of flowering and cultivation, together with a plan of the garden, and he planted show beds to illustrate the Linnaean system of plant classification. In all, the new botanic garden opened with more than 6,000 species. This was a teaching garden in every respect and William Curtis was the chief lecturer; visitors were charged an admission fee. He gave free lectures to subscribers and for an additional fee they could take seeds and plants for their own gardens. In 1789 the Botanic Garden was transferred to a larger site at Brompton.

William Curtis enjoyed lecturing and writing, and his books and treatises were well researched and well received. He had a keen interest in agricultural grasses, collecting and identifying dried specimens for his *Practical observations on the British grasses*, which was to prove useful to the farming community. In 1810 William Aiton named a genus of South African trees of the *Cornaceae* family after him – *Curtisia*.

William Curtis is mainly remembered for *The Botanical Magazine*, first issued in February 1787, which sought to illustrate the plants that gardeners of the day could grow on open ground, in a greenhouse or a stove house. Each monthly part consisted of three hand-coloured plates, drawn and coloured from life by eminent botanical artists. The majority were drawn, coloured and engraved by the young artist Sydenham Edwards, whom William Curtis had specially trained for the task, and each plate had an accompanying text by William himself. The selection of the flowers to be illustrated and discussed was naturally governed by their availability. The gardens of fellow enthusiasts and his own garden provided many of the first specimens. Soon these would be augmented by gifts from nurserymen and from private gardens.

The Botanical Magazine was regularly issued, in spite of wars and other shattering events, and continues to this day. It is said to be the oldest continuously published magazine with coloured illustrations in the world. In 1984, there was a change of title to *The Kew Magazine incorporating Curtis' Botanical Magazine*, but this title has now reverted to the original.

When we did the research for the Quaker Tapestry panel *Quaker Botanists*, it was natural to turn to *The Botanical Magazine* for the illustrations. We used the earliest date, to get as close as possible to the original introductions, even though, for example, the early hydrangea was a dull greenish colour with dark, brownish red centres and nettle-like leaves, very different from the flamboyant specimens of today.

The gifted William Curtis was able to convey his enthusiasm to others and it is therefore no surprise to find several of his family following similar interests. SAMUEL CURTIS (1779–1860), a nurseryman of Lambeth, was his cousin (and also his son-in-law). After the death of William Curtis, Samuel became the publisher of *The Botanical Magazine* and under his leadership maintained its high reputation and scholarly interest.

Samuel Curtis, deeply involved in the publication and with his background as a nurseryman, had a growing interest in the exotic and delicate plants being imported from many parts of the world. Frustrated by the vagaries of the English climate and therefore his inability to cultivate these tender plants, he decided to seek a suitable habitat where he could establish a garden. He acquired the estate of Chateau la Claire on the island of Jersey, fairly wild and barren, and spent several years preparing the site, terracing the steep slopes, bringing in suitable soils and planting trees such as the Monterey pine to provide shelter. He then successfully introduced the tender and exotic plants. There is little of the

Hydrangea arborescens, a detail from the cartoon for 'Quaker Botanists', panel D8 of the Quaker Tapestry

original planting left, but the structure is still there, and the garden is now being rebuilt and replanted, with trees and undergrowth being drastically pruned in order to restore the wonderful sea vistas that Samuel Curtis so enjoyed.

Samuel's son Henry Curtis (therefore William Curtis's grandson) became a noted rose-grower and published a two-volume book *The Beauties of the Rose*. James Mattock, a nurseryman skilled at germinating seeds and raising plants sent from abroad, especially from Australia, married William's sister Mary Curtis.

John Wright Curtis, another of William Curtis's cousins, had a similar, if not as prestigious, career as that of the great botanist. John also went into medicine, training at Edinburgh and returning to Alton to join his father's practice. However, his heart lay in natural history and he is mentioned by Gilbert White, the renowned naturalist of the time, who lived in Alton and published *The natural history of Selborne*. In this book, John Wright Curtis is spoken of as a keen ornithologist and naturalist.

When William Curtis died in 1799 he left his widow and daughter Susannah well provided for and also a magazine which had an excellent reputation. The popularity and esteem for the magazine lies principally in the continued excellence of the botanical artists employed over the 200 years of its publication. It was not until 1948 that a half-tone mechanical process superseded the traditional hand colouring of the plates.

At his death, at the age of fifty-three, William Curtis was mourned by the whole scientific community and by his friends, not only because of his unique contribution to botany, but because his friendships were deep and sincere.

RECORDING THE NATURAL WORLD

One young artist whose life took a far more adventurous path was SYDNEY PARKINSON (1745–1771), the son of a Scottish Quaker brewer. A young man of considerable artistic talents, it is thought that he may well have been a pupil in Edinburgh of a gifted Frenchman who ran the first publicly maintained school of drawing and design in Great Britain, a school at the forefront of drawing and painting from nature which involved learning the structure of plants and animals. Sydney's dream of becoming an artist, however, was shattered when his father's business failed and he was apprenticed to a

family friend, a London woollen merchant.

And so it was that, around 1766, Sydney Parkinson travelled to London, his heart heavier with every mile the stagecoach travelled. His new employer encouraged Sydney to attend the Quaker meeting in the city and there he met James Lee, a Scot like himself. Some of Sydney's early flower paintings were exhibited at the Free Society and had been seen by James Lee, who invited Sydney to his home, the Vineyard Nursery in Hammersmith.

Always pleased to show visitors round his garden, the stove houses, potting sheds and greenhouses, James Lee took Sydney Parkinson on a tour and was immediately impressed by the young man's obvious delight and deep interest in all the plants he saw. Sydney always carried a sketchbook with him and was soon drawing some of the unusual plants, later presenting many of the completed and coloured drawings to James Lee.

Although many Quakers considered artistic and creative pursuits and interests, such as painting and music, unnecessary and frivolous, botanical drawings and paintings were more acceptable because the growing studies of the sciences could result in a deeper knowledge of the wonders of creation and thus of the Creator. There was a great burgeoning of scientific exploration and discussion amongst Quakers. At one time there were more than a dozen Quakers who were Fellows of the Royal Society, their specialities ranging from botany to meteorology, astronomy, crystallography, mineralogy and zoology. Thus Sydney Parkinson was encouraged in his meticulous studies and recording of the natural world which resulted in paintings that were not only detailed and accurate, but works of art in their own right.

A frequent visitor to the Vineyard Nursery was Joseph Banks, a wealthy young landowner with a keen interest in botany. It was in 1767 that James Lee introduced Sydney Parkinson to Joseph Banks, who commissioned Sydney to do paintings of his plant and zoological specimens brought back from a visit to Newfoundland and Labrador. Several of these paintings, chiefly of birds, are now in the National Library of Australia in Canberra and some of Sydney Parkinson's studies of insects made at this time are in the British Museum Natural History collection.

Joseph Banks was quick to recognise the talents of the young man and one evening at the Lees, talking at the fireside, he brought the conversation round to his forthcoming expedition, the proposed voyage of Captain Cook to the South Seas on the ship *Endeavour*.

This expedition had captured the imagination of many and was a topic widely discussed in coffee houses, inns and clubs. Joseph Banks helped to finance the venture, purchasing passages for the scientists and naturalists who were to study the flora and fauna. The eminent Dr Solander was one of the naturalists who had agreed to join the expedition, and now, as Joseph Banks explained, they were looking for botanical artists to record their findings.

It would be a long and arduous voyage, neither comfortable nor safe and Joseph Banks, sitting beside the crackling fire in the Lee home, his feet stretched onto a footstool with a glass of wine in his hand, began to paint a vivid picture of the voyage ahead. He spoke of the storms they would encounter and the possibility of being becalmed for weeks; conditions on board would not be pleasant, with scurvy and dysentery an ever present threat. However, as they were soon to discover on the voyage, in Captain Cook they had a far-seeing and knowledgeable leader who really cared about the well-being of his crew. The Captain believed that by throwing out suspect food, and by including lemons, limes and fresh fruit whenever possible in the daily diet, insisting on a clean ship and the personal cleanliness of the crew, scurvy and similar afflictions could be controlled.

Joseph Banks was enthusiastic about the leadership of Captain Cook, although less so about the good Captain's insistence that when they went ashore all approaches to natives were to be peaceful and with the presentation of gifts. With a wry smile, he added that no doubt this strange idea was a result of Cook being apprenticed to a Quaker ship-owner in Whitby for seven years!

Soon Joseph Banks was vividly describing their likely encounters; natives who were seeing a white man for the first time; strange animals and venomous snakes, spiders and insects; even the plants could hold dangers. Then, turning to Sydney Parkinson, he asked him to consider taking passage as one of the scientific team, as an official botanic artist. He urged the young man to take time to consider all that he had said and to talk with James Lee before giving his answer. Needless to say, Sydney accepted the offer to become one of the two artists.

Sydney Parkinson set sail on the *Endeavour* in 1768. He is described by Beaglehole, Cook's biographer, as 'highly intelligent, sensible and sensitive with long thin fingers and a rather prim little mouth'. (Beaglehole, 1962:28)

Conditions on board were as bad as predicted – cramped, poorly lit, smelly. Joseph Banks and his young protégé shared with the other scientists the cluttered cabin conditions

and the more spacious working area in the Great Cabin. Their common enthusiasm, however, overcame the problems even when, as happened in Rio de Janeiro, the Governor refused permission to go ashore and collect plants. Disregarding this and Captain Cook's orders, they waited for a bright night and then stole off the ship. They rowed noiselessly under cover of darkness to a quiet part of the shore, then crept inland for a mile or so and loaded themselves with over 300 plants, including a passionflower (*Passiflora*), sensitive plant (*Mimosa pudica*) and a poinciana.

The principal objective of the *Endeavour* voyage was to record the Transit of Venus in June 1769 from the recently discovered island of Tahiti, and then, following secret instructions, to explore the Pacific for sight of Terra Incognita Australis – the supposed great land mass of the Southern Hemisphere. The route took them across the Atlantic via Madeira to Brazil, southward to Tierra del Fuego, around Cape Horn and into the Pacific. The recording of the botanical specimens, previously unknown to Europeans, by Joseph Banks and his team proved extremely successful, although that of the Transit was less so. Thus Sydney Parkinson was kept busy drawing the many specimens from each port of call, so many in fact that he used a shorthand method for many, drawing the plant or flower but colouring only partially, with the intention of completing the task on return to London. A great deal of his work covers the flora and fauna of various Pacific islands, New Zealand and the east coast of Australia. It was in this latter region where his most celebrated animal drawing, a sketch of a kangaroo, was made in June 1770 during the time that the *Endeavour* was undergoing repairs at what is now Cooktown.

When they reached Australia, their harvest of new plants was so fruitful that, seeing the hundreds of plants laid out on the sand to be drawn and recorded, Captain Cook named the place Botany Bay. During the three-year voyage Sydney Parkinson made over 900 drawings, sketches and paintings of specimens previously unknown to Europeans.

Only days after reaching Tahiti came the death of Alexander Buchan, the other artist, thus creating additional work for Sydney Parkinson, whose output was prodigious, earning the full appreciation of Joseph Banks and tributes from other crew members who commented on his diligence and unbounded industry. Additionally he maintained a journal which was later published, *A Journal of a Voyage to the South Seas, in his Majesty's Ship, the Endeavour*, and a facsimile of which was published in 1983, *Sydney Parkinson: artist of Cook's Endeavour voyage.*

During the homeward voyage repairs to the *Endeavour* necessitated a stop in Batavia, now Jakarta, during the latter part of 1770. Unfortunately the place was disease ridden, especially with malaria and dysentery and both there, and during the voyage home, a number of the crew became ill and died. Sadly, these were to include Sydney Parkinson, who died on the 26 January 1771 at the young age of twenty-seven years. He was buried at sea.

However his work lives on for on his return to London Joseph Banks employed a team of artists to complete Parkinson's paintings and then had copperplate engravings made which were eventually bequeathed to the British Museum. These were made by a team of eighteen engravers between 1771-84 at a cost of over £7,000 but for some unknown reason no printings were made of these engravings, other than some black impression proofs for Joseph Banks. A few, again in black, were printed in the late nineteenth century and again during the twentieth century. Then in the latter part of the twentieth century 738 of the botanical engravings were published by the Natural History Department of the British Museum as a part-work under the title *Banks' Florilegium*. Thus Joseph Banks's collection and Sydney Parkinson's paintings from the *Endeavour* voyage can now be seen in great accuracy of shape and colour.

Ficus parkinsonii was named in Sydney Parkinson's memory.

'THE BEST NATURAL HISTORY PAINTER IN ENGLAND'

An intriguing young person flits in and out of the scene at this time, one of a very small number of women working in the field of botany. She is ANN LEE, daughter of James Lee of the Vineyard Nursery. She must have been a great joy to him, absorbing his interest and love of plants, and steadily building a sound academic knowledge, not only of botany, but also of animal life, and insects in particular.

In the previous section we read about Sydney Parkinson and his journey on the *Endeavour* with Captain Cook. Sydney was engaged by James Lee to give thirteen-year-old Ann lessons in drawing and flower painting. No doubt James Lee and Sydney Parkinson were at first amused, watching Ann copy Sydney's intense study of each part of the plant, but she was a talented and competent pupil and her interest and abilities as a botanical artist flourished.

Another visitor to the home and nursery garden of James Lee was Carl Thunberg, the Swedish naturalist, and in 1778 he wrote 'At Mr Lees I likewise saw his daughter's fine collection of insect paintings'. Fabricius wrote of her as 'the best natural history painter in England'. (Fabricius 1782)

The insects she painted were vital and alive, as were her flower studies, meticulous in their detail but also possessing a rare sense of movement. E. J.Willson comments on her 'minute attention to detail so that, for example, every tiny hair of a saxifrage stands out distinct and separate'. (Willson 1961:60)

Later Ann Lee became a botanical artist in her own right, illustrating the catalogues of the Vineyard Nursery and attracting the attention of William Curtis. We find several plates in *The Botanical Magazine* signed either Ann Lee or A.L. She was one of the five eminent artists commissioned by John Fothergill to make drawings on vellum of some of the flowers in his gardens, each flower to be drawn and painted at the peak of its perfection. It is recorded that after the death of John Fothergill over 2,000 paintings were sold to the Empress Catherine II of Russia for £2,300. Sixteen of Ann's paintings of Mesembryanthemum are in the British Museum, and Ann's family owns around 100 other paintings.

A PROLIFIC
EDUCATOR

PRISCILLA BELL WAKEFIELD (1751–1832)
was an aunt of Elizabeth Fry, both following in
the tradition of strong-minded women, blessed
with a liberal Quaker education and an
independence unusual for women in the
eighteenth and nineteenth centuries.

Priscilla Wakefield was a contemporary of
William Curtis, the daughter of a successful
coal merchant from Stamford Hill, Tottenham.
She married Edward Wakefield of London at
the age of twenty and had five children, only
three of whom reached adulthood. Doubtless
she was largely responsible for the early
education of her own children, and realised
that specially written and often amusing books
could capture their interest. She wrote moral
tales, travelogues, and simple but accurate
books on general education, enlivening them
with anecdotes. They were aimed at specific
age groups, as was the current vogue in
education. During the years 1794–1817 she
wrote seventeen books; nearly all were for
children but increasingly her readership
widened, and the bookshelves of the middle
class invariably held some of her writings.

Many of her books, often written in the form
of letters between sisters, or conversations
between parent and child, covered natural
history. In her early letters she decorously
avoids the use of sexual terms in her
description of plants and their propagation,
but she later embraces the Linnaean system of
classification and overcomes her modesty. In
1796 she wrote a pioneering book on botany
(*Introduction to Botany*) in which she explains
this system. She wanted to write a book of
moderate price, divested as much as possible of
technical terms, with an easily understandable
text. It was so successful that it went through
several editions in England and America, was
translated into French and was updated several
years later to take account of changing ideas
about plant taxonomy. In the book she urges
the study of botany as 'a substitute for some of
the trifling, not to say pernicious, objects, that
too frequently occupy the leisure time of young
ladies of fashionable manners'. (Wakefield,
1796:v)

In 1816 she added a book on the
classification of insects, always aiming at
simplicity and accuracy spiced with anecdotes
and humour. She commented frequently on the
spiritual benefits of nature study in her *Juvenile
Anecdotes* (1795–1798), a book of moral tales,
and she showed her disapproval in her books of
parents who allowed their children to become
frivolous.

Apart from writing, Priscilla Wakefield kept
herself busy in philanthropic projects. She
founded the Green Coat School of Industry for
Girls, a lying-in charity for poor women
approaching childbirth, and a Penny Bank for
Children which historians consider to be the
beginning of savings banks in England.

Inevitably Priscilla Wakefield's books went
out of fashion, but in recent years documents
by and about Priscilla Wakefield have been
collected together in the Friends House
Library, London, as the Hazel Mews Papers.

Quaker plantsmen and collectors

MAN OF THE TREES

THOMAS STORY (c.1670–1742) had a passion for trees – trees by the thousand, all shapes, sizes and varieties, from this country and abroad.

A lawyer by profession, Thomas Story was a strong link between the Quakers in the New World and those at home. He became a Quaker after meeting George Fox and William Penn, and then began extensive travels carrying the Quaker message in Britain and in Ireland (where he was imprisoned). He then decided to go to the New World, originally planning to stay for just two years. In 1698 he arrived on the island of Nantucket, where there was a growing group of Quakers. The story of this whaling community, their refusal to take up arms for either side in the American War of Independence and their subsequent exodus to Milford Haven in Wales in 1792, is told in 'Nantucket and Milford Haven', panel F12 of the Quaker Tapestry.

He stayed with the Quakers on Nantucket Island until 1700 and then travelled on to Philadelphia where he met again with William Penn, the founder of Pennsylvania. William Penn successfully persuaded him to make use of his legal knowledge in the service of the new community and Thomas Story stayed for fourteen years as Master of the Rolls, Land Commissioner and member of the Council, as well as travelling extensively in the ministry.

Thomas Story was an arborealist rather than a plantsman. His interest was probably stimulated by William Penn, who had a large number of trees sent out from Britain for his garden in America – fruit trees and hawthorns, and nut trees such as walnut and hazel all grew alongside indigenous trees purchased, as we read in his accounts, principally from Maryland. A carpet of wild flowers was planted under the tree canopy.

Thomas Story, in his journal, records his arrival in Philadelphia. His intention was to meet with fellow Quakers and to travel together to Yearly Meeting, the regular gathering of the Religious Society of Friends,

to be held that year in Maryland. He found that a form of yellow fever was rife in the city and that many Quakers had already died of the virulent disease – as many as eight each day for many weeks. It was decided, however, that the Yearly Meeting in Maryland should go ahead as planned and Thomas records that, although the fever was at its height, not one person fell ill during the days of the meeting.

Edward Shippen and his wife were amongst those who were stricken with the disease and recovered. A Quaker merchant originally from Yorkshire, Edward Shippen later became the first Mayor of Philadelphia. He was known for three things – he was the biggest man in Philadelphia, he lived in the biggest house and he rode in the biggest carriage! (Moore, 1947:99) The Quakers who were to travel together to attend the Yearly Meeting in Maryland met at the home of Edward Shippen to make their arrangements. It was on this occasion that Thomas Story first met Ann Shippen, the daughter of the house. Shippen explained that Ann would not be going with the party to Yearly Meeting as she was only fifteen. Thomas Story was twenty-nine, but it was probably not much later when he and James Logan vied with each other for her affections.

The rivalry was not friendly and several of their Quaker friends, including William Penn, remonstrated with the two rivals, who avoided one another for years. William Penn Junior writes to James Logan: 'I am sorry that you are like to be unsure in your amours; I assure you, you have my good wishes and should have my assistance were I there.' (Moore, 1947:106) Ann herself seems to have settled the matter by choosing Thomas Story and they were married in July 1705 when Ann would have been about twenty-one.

After that the two men became not only reconciled but good friends for the rest of their lives, corresponding regularly, and we have their letters on such diverse subjects as the germination of seeds and world politics. In one letter, Thomas Story writes that he had 'been at Scarborough [England] for some months and studied the great variation of strata in the high

opposite
Fritillaria camschatcensis
Anne Dent

23

cliffs'. (Moore, 1947:105) He had also discussed a theory based on a long observation that the earth was much older than the theologians believed from their reading of the Bible. Another of his scientific studies led him to the conclusion that apparently solid inert matter was made up of numberless moving particles. He was, indeed, a man before his time.

When Thomas Story married Ann Shippen they were given the 'biggest house' as a wedding present, and lived 'in great harmony and affection' (Moore, 1947:91) until her early death six or seven years later. During this time, Thomas Story was often away travelling in the ministry but in 1714 he decided to return to England via Barbados, renewing the many friendships made on an earlier visit to the West Indies in 1707. James Logan and his wife took over the Thomas Story's house and we have a delightful domestic letter he sent to Thomas Story: 'My wife can no longer be reconciled to the kitchen, which, by reason of its smallness has ever been inconvenient but it is now so much decayed that it cannot otherwise be mended than by a new one . . . But this would cost at least one hundred pounds, for the pump also must be removed and so ought the little house [the outside privy].' (Moore, 1947:100)

On his return to England Thomas Story met Peter Collinson, and the two men formed a deep and lasting friendship. The rather bashful Peter Collinson, who found it difficult to discuss his faith, found in Thomas Story a confidant, a sympathetic ear and a wise counsellor.

In 1722 Thomas Story bought Justice Town, the family estate near Carlisle, from his widowed sister-in-law and here he proceeded to plant both British and American trees from seeds received from Peter Collinson. Thomas Story frequently received horticultural advice from Peter Collinson as on this occasion when he also received some young saplings: 'I have taken what care I could in packing them up in moss with as much earth about their roots as the fibres would hold and if thee art cautious in undoing the box and moss no doubt they'll scarcely miss their removal. Gett the ground immediately ready to plant them and in the box is some seed from Virginia.' (Moore, 1947:13) We believe the saplings were Ferroscarlet chestnuts and the seed, as Collinson wrote, 'came from Penns' – presumably from 'Pennsbury', the name of William Penn's garden in Philadelphia.

Although Thomas Story was enthusiastic about tree planting and spreading the idea of growing woods, forests, and avenues wherever it was possible, nevertheless he felt conscious that his first and most pressing involvement should continue to be spreading the message of Quakerism. He referred to his arboreal interests as his 'amusements', but we believe that he encouraged the development of arboreta in this country by introducing rich landowners to the importance of trees and by selling them saplings and seeds to make this possible.

Thomas Story was absent from Justice Town for nearly twelve years, on Quaker business, and returned to find his own woods overgrown and neglected. He began to remedy the situation: 'With many hands I began to plant out several sorts of young trees, as oaks, elms, ashes, acer-majors, poplars of several kinds, firs, English walnuts, black walnuts, tulip trees, locust trees, cedars of America, occidental planes, lindels, chestnuts, horse-chestnuts, diverse sorts of willows, beeches, hornbeams, scarlet oaks, etc, which I had raised from seed and cuttings, to furnish that part of the country, in time, with timber, which is now scarce, that I might be an example to others in that useful kind of improvement which several have since started to follow.' (Moore, 1947:14)

Amongst the 'several' whose gardens and estates received trees from Thomas Story, and possibly also through Peter Collinson, was the Earl of Carlisle, a school friend of Thomas's and owner of Castle Howard in Yorkshire, where there are still some trees unusual in Britain such as the flowering hickories.

The travels of this energetic man through Britain, Ireland, Europe and the New World, his friendships and his firm adherence to Quakerism, as well as the story of his more personal life and 'amusements', of his overwhelming love and knowledge of the environment and of his almost prophetic understanding of the implications if woodland was mishandled are all told in Emily Moore's book *Travelling with Thomas Story*. It makes fascinating reading, especially since we feel that in spite of the passing centuries we are still struggling with concern for the environment.

Thomas Story died in 1742 and was buried in the Quaker burial ground at Carlisle. Many local friends attended the large funeral, and others from further afield. The Meeting for Worship was a celebration and thanksgiving for the life of a man of integrity, energy and diversity whose legacy and example add him firmly to the list of Quakers who helped to change our gardens and parks, and who expanded our understanding of natural history. A large tulip tree (opposite) is still growing in the lawn at Justice Town, his home near Carlisle, as are several of the types of trees planted by Thomas Story, 'Man of the Trees'.

SOWING THE SEEDS OF FRIENDSHIP

Three men in particular, all avid collectors of new plants, had a lasting effect on the introduction of new plants to our gardens from all over the world. John Fothergill and John Coakley Lettsom were hard working and dedicated doctors; Peter Collinson ran a successful business as a mercer and woollen exporter. They were all members of the Religious Society of Friends but with very different personalities.

Their common interest in and enthusiasm for natural history must have provided a completely new avenue and respite from their hectic life styles, even though, in pursuit of their enthusiasm for plants, they often found an equally demanding taskmaster.

PETER COLLINSON (1693–1768) grabbed his coat from the wooden hook, jammed his broad-brimmed hat on his head and rushed down the two flights of stairs from his office into the basement of his premises, a mercer's business at the sign of the Red Lion in London's Gracechurch Street – a scene repeated several times a year and we can imagine the bustle and the excitement.

As he ran down the stairs, Peter Collinson called out 'Reuben, John, Seth, bring a handcart each and follow me to the docks! There's a consignment waiting for us. The ship docked an hour ago.' and off he hurried, leading a procession of three carts, clanking over the cobbles.

'Why the haste?' said Reuben. 'Yon ship has been on the high seas for three weeks or more. One hour won't make much difference, I reckon.'

But Peter Collinson was anxious to see the condition of the precious cargo and eager to see the horticultural treasures which had arrived from the New World. The little procession headed back to the mercer's premises, the carts carrying wooden cases hooped over with canvas covers and containers sealed with wax, with Peter Collinson, Quaker, botanist, naturalist, plant hunter, gardener and business man, bringing up the rear.

The carts were wheeled down a slope into the basement of the mercer's premises. 'Seth lad, set the big tables under the window, cover them well with thick fresh paper and bring up one of the carts. We'll sort out that one first, I think, the one with five boxes. John, thee knows where I keep my magnifying glass, forceps, knives and trowels . . . and Reuben, I need my large plant journal, quills and ink and sand pot, and of course, my letterbook. Later,

Tulip tree in flower

I'll have the list of subscribers and new boxes for packing the plants. Quickly about it, lads. We have a lot of work today.'

The lads were not averse to leaving their job of packing bales of woollen material to join Peter Collinson in the task he was obviously going to enjoy – sorting out, checking identifications, labelling and allocating plants and seeds to one of the subscribers to his box scheme and meticulously recording them. His lists can be seen today in the Herbarium at the British Museum.

There was a cry from Reuben: 'Peter Collinson, there's a different sort of box here. It says f-r-a-g-ile live an-i-mals.' Peter left his table to view the shallow wooden box, the sides and the lid were bored with holes and in John Bartram's writing, 'Turtles' eggs, for my very good friend, Peter' and on the lid and one of the sides, 'FRAGILE – LIVE ANIMALS'.

Peter Collinson's eyes danced with anticipation. What had John sent this time? Carefully, he prised open the lid and to his delight saw, cradled in moss, fifteen turtle eggs. Their shells, leathery and therefore not as fragile as the eggs of birds, ensured that they had arrived safely. Even as Peter Collinson peered at them he saw one egg move, then split and, with impeccable timing, the first baby turtle started to hatch.

'Lads, over here,' shouted Peter. But he had no need to call them, they were already crowding round the table, and soon four rapt faces were poring over the box, silent and scarcely breathing as yet another little turtle began to emerge from the egg.

25

Peter Collinson

'Their eyes are closed tight, like kittens', observed Seth.

'Watch', said Peter Collinson quietly, and even as they looked, the first one started to scrabble at his eyes, forcing them open.

'They've no mother to look after them as they hatch', explained their employer, 'and they have to fend for themselves straight away, so they need their eyes.'

'You were right to go to the ship in the Pool, these might have died if we had waited,' observed John.

The four could scarcely tear themselves from the box, although Peter was soon consulting his books to read how best to look after these tiny creatures. The next day he wrote to John Bartram to thank him for the seeds and plants and to express his delight at the gift of turtle eggs: '[How] artfully they disengaged themselves from the shell and then with their forefeet scratched their eyes open.' (Brett-James, 1925:131)

It was October 1737 and the morning's activities were not unusual. Peter Collinson was an avid and knowledgeable botanist and used some of the profits from his thriving wholesale mercer's business to further his studies and his delight in nature – plant life in particular. His trade with the New World also gave him the opportunity to correspond with other enthusiasts there and to pester them for seeds and plants unknown in this country. Although largely self-taught, his scientific skills

were much respected, and he was elected to the Royal Societies in London, Berlin and Sweden.

In the eighteenth century the sciences of botany and natural history were developing fast. No longer were people willing to believe that the Barnacle tree shed its fruits as living birds (hence the name Barnacle Goose as stated in Gerard's *Herball*). The great naturalist Gilbert White of Selborne and Dr Johnson also held this view, and a much respected seventeenth-century naturalist, John Josselyn, stated that 'barley … commonly degenerates into oats'. (Josselyn, 1672:88)

Even the Swedish botanist Linnaeus held the belief that swallows hibernate under water in winter. He was not alone in this and he entered into a lengthy scientific argument with Peter Collinson, who asked Linnaeus to show him the organs that allowed a swallow to live under water. The Swedish naturalist would never admit his error, although the Linnaean Society has the book *Regnum Animale*, written by Linnaeus, in which the statement about hibernating swallows is crossed out, obviously by the author himself.

The new scientific outlook provided the opportunity for a fresh scientific appraisal of the whole of plant life. It was Linnaeus, with his classification based on the numbers of stamens and pistils and the use of only two names for each plant, who gained the interest and support of many contemporary botanists. However some, including Peter Collinson, were slower to respond.

Peter Collinson enjoyed the friendship of Benjamin Franklin, Sir Hans Sloane, Philip Miller, Thomas Story, and John Fothergill, as well as that of families who were rich enough to indulge their love of gardens and their interest in the new and exotic plants from many parts of the world; it was the golden age of plant hunters. Peter Collinson provided the link between those intrepid explorers and the rich patrons such as Lord Petre, the Dukes of Richmond, Bedford and Norfolk, the dowager Princess of Wales for the botanic garden at Kew and also the King for the Hampton Court gardens. Yet Peter Collinson always retained his simple way of life and seems to have possessed that inestimable gift of friendship by enjoying shared interests.

With his scratchy quill he wrote many hundreds of letters, revealing not only his intense enthusiasm and extensive knowledge of living plants and creatures, but also his personal involvement with his correspondents, many of whom were plant hunters. In return for his encouragement and financial support, they provided him with seeds, bulbs and plants from many parts of the world. Some he planted

opposite
Papaver nudicaule
Audrey Jennett

in his own garden, first in Peckham and then at Mill Hill – others he passed on to other enthusiasts or donated to help establish collections at Kew, at the Chelsea Physic Garden or to provide dried specimens for the British Museum.

Peter Collinson received seeds and plants from Father d'Incarville, a French Jesuit missionary working in China, including a Tree of Heaven (*Ailanthus altissima*), and a hornbeam (probably *Carpinus orientalis*) from Persia via Dr Mounsey in St Petersburg. Count Demidoff of St Petersburg, owner of an iron mine and extensive gardens in West Siberia, sent 'a lily as black as any flower I have ever seen'. From yet another correspondent in Russia he received the Iceland poppy (*Papaver nudicaule*, previous page) and *Fritillaria camschatcensis* (p.22) with delicate bell-like flowers of vivid purple, and from Dr Ammann, founder of the Botanic Garden in St Petersburg, came the blue butterfly larkspur (*Delphinium grandiflorum*) and red-barked dogwood (*Cornus alba*).

His correspondence led to an interchange of seeds, bulbs and plants between England and many foreign and colonial countries. To John Custis of Williamsburg in America (whose widowed daughter-in-law Martha married George Washington) he sent tulips, crown imperials, carnations, hyacinths, asters and lilies. There are letters over several years between the two men, a correspondence apparently started in 1734 with an unexpected gift from John Custis to Peter Collinson of a mountain primrose, plant and seeds sent on two different ships for safety. In return Peter Collinson sent some horse chestnuts, having heard that although Custis was educated in England, he could not recollect seeing a horse-chestnut tree or the fruits. In the same letter he sent a recipe for almond tart and a request for three or four plants of dogwood (*Cornus virginica*) and also: 'a sort of laurel or bay that bears borders of flowers not much unlike the *Laurus tinus*. It is by some improperly called ivy and if the sheep eat it, it kills them'. Lewis Dillwyn, when compiling *Hortus Collinsonianus*, a list of plant introductions made by Peter Collinson, names this as '*Kalmia angustifolia L.*, commonly known as ivy'.

Towards the end of 1737 Peter Collinson wrote to John Custis warning of a visit by John Bartram: 'a downright plain countryman. His conversations you'll find compensate for his appearance'. (Swem, 1948:66) Eighteen months later a letter from John Custis tells of the visit from John Bartram: 'he is the most takeing facetious man I have ever met with and

never was so much delighted with a stranger in all my life'. (Swem, 1948:77)

Alongside discussions about plants, seeds, bulbs and their propagation we read of Peter Collinson's real concern for his friend's health. John Custis had been seriously ill and Peter wrote: 'I take it your late illness was an effort of Nature to discharge and overcome some Malignitys that may have been latent for some time – humour her, take gentle exercise, a moderate light easy dyet, broths, refreshing drinks, milk morn'g and even. It warm from the cow…. So, my good friend, if you find yourself hippish or low-spirited, endeavour all you can, by gentle exercise and a constant applycation to something diverting to disperse those mists and clouds, for the mind affects the body. I am at times intolerably affected with a headach, but a gentle vomitt is to mee an instant and most effective cure.' (Swem, 1948:80) The next sentence is about sorrel trees and a paragraph later is advice on how to deal with moles.

Sometimes he describes his many correspondents as 'brothers of the spade' and from these letters we realise the friendships and co-operation which existed from country to country. They were all eager to help each other, giving freely of their time and advice, relating both their horticultural successes and their failures.

Another friend was Benjamin Franklin, who made many trips to London and never failed to bring with him some new treasure for Peter who was responsible, along with John Fothergill, for Franklin's introduction to the Royal Society in London, and for the publication of his experiments in electricity. Peter Collinson actually shipped to America the apparatus that enabled Benjamin Franklin to make his first experiments in this field.

Peter Collinson's most assiduous and prolific correspondence was with John Bartram, a fellow Quaker and self-taught botanist from Pennsylvania, and later with John's son William Bartram.

At the age of seventy-two, reminiscing about the box scheme, Peter Collinson wrote of his early frustrations as he tried to persuade his colleagues in foreign countries to provide him with plants: 'What was common with them but rare with us they did not think worth sending. Thus I laboured in vain or to little purpose for some years and obtained but few seed or plants, neither money nor friendship would tempt them.' (Brett-James, 1925:52)

Eventually he heard about John Bartram, a farmer of Philadelphia, possibly from Thomas Story. A good businessman and well used to trade with America Peter Collinson organised a group of subscribers in London, all plantsmen. He employed John Bartram to gather plants and seeds for subscribers who agreed to buy boxes of plants, bulbs and seeds, each box to contain 100 to 105 new introductions at a cost of five guineas (later raised to ten guineas) per box. From one letter we gather that the listing of plants and the provision of the boxes of plants and seeds was not the end of Collinson's interest: 'I forgot to mention that after I had supplied the several persons in the lists with seeds the next was "Pray sir, how and in what manner must I sow them? Pray be so good as to give me some directing for my gardener is an ignorant fellow"!' (Brett-James, 1925:53)

The first subscriber was Lord Petre, who grew the earliest recorded camellia in Britain and planted some 40,000 trees on his estate. His garden, arboretum and stove houses contained 1,000 American trees, and many plants and trees new to Britain such as pineapples, guavas, ginger and limes. When Lord Petre died of smallpox at the age of twenty-nine, Peter Collinson wrote to John Bartram of his grief. John Bartram then sent to the widow the nest of a humming-bird, and in return Lady Petre sent to Bartram a pear tree which was still surviving in the twentieth century in Bartram's garden in Philadelphia, now famous as the first botanic garden in America. Peter Collinson also wrote of his joy when Lord Petre's son grew up and ordered his first box of plants: 'It may truly be said that the spirit of Elijah rests upon Elisha!' (Darlington, 1849:232)

The second and third Dukes of Richmond often sought the advice of Peter Collinson and were subscribers to the box scheme. The second Duke successfully germinated and raised to maturity some seeds of the magnolia sent in the very first consignment. For the third Duke, who hoped to 'clothe the naked hills at Goodwood', Collinson purchased 1,000 cedars of Lebanon at a cost of £79 6s; some of these still survive at the Goodwood racecourse.

Sir Hans Sloane was another close friend, whose collection of curios and antiques formed the nucleus of the British Museum. He asked Peter Collinson to arrange the Natural History section of his collection, and eventually added dried plants and seeds as they were sent by John Bartram.

Collinson was a friend and correspondent of Linnaeus (the genus *Collinsonia* was coined by Linnaeus to commemorate his friend), and frequently sent specimens to him for classification. He sent to Linnaeus two trumpet-shaped leaves of a *Sarracenia*, a pitcher-plant which he called one of the wonders of the vegetable world.

He received and distributed plants from all over the world, growing many in his own garden at Mill Hill. It is now a public school, with a few of the trees planted by Collinson preserved today, including a Portuguese laurel, a variegated holly, a deciduous cypress and hemlock spruce. There are more than fifty plants recorded in the unpublished *Hortus Collinsonianus* as being new introductions to this country growing in his garden. These include shooting star (*Dodecatheon meadia*, right), phlox, kalmias and azaleas, as well as medicinal plants – witch hazels (*Hamamelis virginiana*), turmeric root (*Hydrastis canadensis*), senna (*Cassia marilandica*) and snake root (*Cimicifuga racemosa*).

It is Lewis Dillwyn (1778–1855) whom we have to thank for the record of the plant introductions made by Collinson. *Hortus Collinsonianus* (1809) was prepared by Dillwyn and eventually published privately in 1843. His father, George Dillwyn, was amongst the many Welsh Quakers who had emigrated to America to work with William Penn, the founder of Pennyslvania, becoming one of the foremost anti-slavery workers. At the age of thirty, George Dillwyn returned to England where he continued his fight for the abolition of slavery. His son Lewis Weston Dillwyn was born in Ipswich and educated at a Quaker School, where he became absorbed in the study of natural history in general and botany in particular. He explored and recorded the flora in many parts of England and Wales, and in recognition of the thoroughness and accuracy of his observations and writing, he was made a Fellow of the Royal Society in 1804. The genus *Dillwynia* was named after him.

John Bartram and Peter Collinson became good friends, sharing their religious beliefs, firm in their Quakerism (although John Bartram's Quakerism didn't always find favour with his meeting). They corresponded for over 35 years, yet they never met. They discussed the difficulties and possible solutions to the problems of transporting seeds, plants and small saplings, first as collected in the wild, and then the difficulties of shipping. They speculated on bird migration and exchanged eggs – not always birds' eggs, as we know.

In a letter to John Bartram in February 1737, Peter Collinson began by answering a complaint that he had not replied to a query about insect attack on Bartram's stone fruit: 'I never heard that it was insects that mazed your Plums, Apricots and Nectarines. If they are at the root, water that had tobacco leaves soaked in it will kill them, by making a basin round the tree and watering it frequently with this

Shooting star *Dodecatheon meadia*, a detail from the cartoon for 'Quaker Botanists', panel D8 of the Quaker Tapestry

water.' (Darlington, 1849:85) In the same letter Peter Collinson suggests a method of keeping plants fresh when collecting in the wild: 'Take three or four largest ox-bladders; cut off the neck high and when a plant is found take it up with a little earth with the roots, put this in the bladder, then put water in the bladder to cover the roots; then tie the neck of the bladder around the stalk of the plant, leaving the leaves, flowers etc, without. Large plants won't do so well, but several small plants may be put in a bladder. When tied hang it to the pummel or skirts of the saddle or any other convenient way thee may choose.' (Darlington, 1849:87)

We read of the temptation facing Dr Witt, a physician and correspondent of Collinson, apparently entrusted with the task of carrying some Lady's Slipper orchids from John Bartram. Peter Collinson had received a flimsy excuse for their non-arrival: 'I am afraid the old gentleman has been too cunning for thee. But these fine Lady's Slippers, do not let them escape, for they are my favourite plants. I have your yellow one but I much want the other sorts. Pray show the Doctor no more. Don't say anything I have writ, neither shall I take any notice of thine!' (Darlington, 1849:87)

We know that Peter Collinson, being a mercer, sent material to Bartram to be made into clothing for his family. It was wrapped in a thick heavy paper which John Bartram's wife presumably sewed into bags which the plant hunter carried, to store and separate the seeds he gathered each autumn. John Bartram writes to thank Peter Collinson for 'a drugget coat, black waistcoat and shagg breeches, also a calico gown for my wife ... all much to my taste'. (Darlington, 1849:190)

John Bartram had written to Peter Collinson about a proposed plant-hunting expedition to Virginia, and thanked Peter for suggestions about friends with whom he might stay, one of whom was John Custis of Williamsburg. A reply from Peter Collinson shows the depth of their friendship for one was able to write and the other to accept, without offence, suggestions for John Bartram's conduct on the proposed journey:
'One thing I must desire of thee, and do insist that thee oblige me therein; That thou make up that drugget cloth to go to Virginia in, and not appear to disgrace thyself or me; for though I should not esteem thee the less, to come to me in what dress thou will, yet these Virginians are a very gentle, well-dressed people, and look, perhaps, more at a man's outside than his inside. For these and other reasons pray go very clean, neat and handsomely dressed to Virginia. Never mind thy clothes; I will send

some more another year.' (Brett-James, 1925:129-30)

To the great delight of his father, Michael Collinson was also a keen botanist and naturalist, writing to many of his father's friends. It is from Michael that we read of his father's great distress when precious plants were stolen from Mill Hill not once, but three times. Peter Collinson died in 1768 and was buried in the Quaker burial ground in Bermondsey. It was closed for burials in 1896 and later made into an open space for the citizens of Bermondsey. It is now a children's playground with borders, bright with flowers, some of which were introduced into our gardens by Peter Collinson. He would have been happy.

TWO BARRELS OF EARTH

JOHN FOTHERGILL (1712–80) arrived home at Upton Park after an absence of two or three weeks spent both visiting patients and on Quaker business. It was late in the evening but James, his head gardener, knew that the doctor would value a walk around the garden and he was prepared with a lantern. The two men walked slowly, John Fothergill still in his travelling clothes with a thick cloak, James in moleskin trousers tied around his calves, and a thick sheepskin jerkin to protect against the chill night air. The doctor specifically asked to see the azaleas and kalmias (left) that Humphry Marshall had sent from Philadelphia, and James was able to assure John Fothergill that only two plants had not survived – he thought slugs or a mouse at the roots might have been the cause.

As they walked round the garden, one of the two men would stoop to pick up a slug or snail whose tell-tale silvery trail shone in the rays of the lantern. Probably their walk extended to the recently planted saplings on the edge of the wood, leaving the stove house and its treasures closed against the chilly night, to be enjoyed the next morning. Often this lantern-lit tour round his garden was the only time in which the busy doctor could relax amongst his treasured plants and talk with his gardener.

John Fothergill's garden at Upton was especially noted for its collection of North American plants. He made a mental note to write to Humphry Marshall, a cousin of John Bartram, explaining the care and attention he lavished upon a large border devoted to these plants, planting them in 'rich, black turf-like soil, mixed with sand, and protecting them with a warm covering of fern'. (Fox,

Kalmia latifolia, a detail from the cartoon for 'Quaker Botanists', panel D8 of the Quaker Tapestry

1919:194) He lists kalmias, azaleas, the Umbrella tree (*Magnolia tripetala*), which flowered abundantly and grew over twenty feet high but wrote that he was waiting for the first flowering of the *Magnolia grandiflora* (right).

In America, Humphry Marshall made a botanic garden with a stove house and a small observatory and he certainly collected for John Fothergill from about 1767. He sent insects and animals and we read of a live snake seized by Customs! In John Fothergill's directions for sending stuffed birds, Marshall is advised to disembowel the birds, and after drying, stuff the skins of the smaller birds 'with tow and tobacco dust, or if the skins were large, with salt or pepper'. (Fox, 1919:192) In return John Fothergill sent books, a telescope and a thermometer, as well as money to further Marshall's studies.

Marshall also sent plants to Casper Wistar, a Quaker doctor of German descent who had settled in New Jersey. The climbing plant Wisteria (*Wisteria sinensis*, p.40) should more correctly be named 'Wistaria', for it is named after Casper Wistar, who succeeded Thomas Jefferson as president of the American Philosophical Society.

The variety, depth and breadth of John Fothergill's interests would impress any reader. He was a Yorkshireman, born in Wensleydale in 1712 into a Quaker family, educated at Sedbergh Grammar School and then apprenticed to Benjamin Bartlett, a Bradford Quaker and a well-known and respected apothecary. Bartlett was an excellent botanist, very knowledgeable about medicinal herbs as were all apothecaries, and he found in John Fothergill an apt pupil. His indenture papers stated that 'his master he shall well and faithfully serve, his secrets he shall keep.

Taverns he shall not haunt, at dice, cards, bowls or other unlawful games he shall not play.' (Fox, 1919:11) After six years of his apprenticeship, spent learning botany, mixing medicines and salves and visiting patients, John Fothergill decided to enter the comparatively new University of Edinburgh as Oxford and Cambridge did not open their doors to Quakers or other dissenters until the 1870s.

John Fothergill's grandfather had left him £120 for his education, so he set off on horseback for the three-day journey to Scotland. He spent 17s 6d on food, lodging, fodder and stabling en route, and then sold his horse for four guineas in Edinburgh. Here he paid 2s 6d per week to his landlady and recorded all his expenses in a little account book, preserved in the archives of Ackworth School near Pontefract, Yorkshire, a school which John Fothergill later helped to establish.

In 1736 John Fothergill took a degree, not as an apothecary but as a Doctor of Medicine. He then travelled by sea to London, a journey that took eight days and cost just over a guinea. Here he enrolled at St Thomas' Hospital to begin a two-year course in practical medicine and hospital procedures. On completion of his medical studies he travelled to Holland, then at the forefront of medicine, and worked in several medical centres before returning to London to set up his own practice. At the age of thirty-six he added to his growing reputation by writing a treatise on the treatment of the ulcerated sore throat (Scarlatina), a life-threatening illness very prevalent at this time and often occurring in epidemic proportions.

All through his career he was always willing and eager to investigate and evaluate any new discoveries and treatments. About twenty years later he was consulted by Catherine the Great of Russia about the choice of a doctor who would be prepared to inoculate her and her whole family against smallpox. John Fothergill recommended Dr Dimsdale, a Quaker disowned for marrying out (until 1860 Quaker marriages were legal only if they were to fellow-Quakers). Dr Dimsdale must be the only Quaker with the title Baron, which was bestowed on him by the grateful Catherine of Russia. Although officially no longer a Quaker he continued to attend Quaker Meetings for worship and was buried in the Quaker Burial Ground at Bishop's Stortford.

A few years later John Fothergill was 'too busy' to accept the post of physician to King George III. He was a successful doctor, introducing many new treatments and often making over £7,000 a year. This large income

left
John Fothergill

Magnolia grandiflora
a detail from the cartoon for
'Quaker Botanists',
panel D8 of the
Quaker Tapestry

he spent freely and wisely – the fees of his affluent patients paid for his free clinics and work with the poor of London. He travelled many miles to visit his patients, rich and poor alike, and when we remember that these journeys would be made on horseback, by carriage or on foot, we wonder that he had much time or energy left.

Yet John Fothergill's other interests and enthusiasms were a vital part of his life; he was an active member of the Society of Friends, being three times Clerk of London Yearly Meeting, a responsible and demanding position, and he also undertook many commitments on behalf of the Society. A keen educationalist, he helped to set up Ackworth School in Yorkshire, and contributed money and advice towards organising Quaker schools in Pennsylvania and Rhode Island, New York. Libraries were an essential element in the spread of education in the New World and John Fothergill helped to meet this need by sending books from England.

He was a Fellow of the Royal Society and gave papers on such diverse subjects as conchology, corals, insects and amber, backed up by carefully catalogued collections. Along with Peter Collinson, he introduced Benjamin Franklin's work on electricity to the Royal Society, and through this friendship allied himself with Franklin against the War of Independence. In addition to this attempt at reconciliation John Fothergill set up a national subscription to feed and clothe the victims of that war, be they friend or foe.

Back in London he actively supported the work of the prison reformer John Howard – his work amongst the poor people of London had made him acutely aware of their living (and dying) conditions. Consequently he became politically active to attempt to introduce sanitary regulations which would inevitably improve their health. The Howard League for Penal Reform is named after John Howard. Between 1775 and 1790 John Howard made seven journeys across Europe in search of a humane prison system for English gaols to follow. He conducted these investigations on his own and financed them himself.

John Fothergill and Peter Collinson shared a deep and lasting lifetime friendship. The two friends were passionately interested in the introduction of unusual and rare plants from all over the world into our gardens and parks, as were many men and women at that time. Seeing the success of Peter Collinson's garden, John Fothergill resolved to follow suit and buy a plot for a garden, although he was disappointed over his first choice of land,

realising that the tenant was dependent upon that particular piece of ground for the subsistence of his family. However he continued with the purchase but gave the land over to the astonished tenant.

Nevertheless this had strengthened his resolve to create his own garden and needing no further urging from Peter Collinson we find the two friends, in 1762, in a coach bound for Essex, where, through one of his medical friends, he had been able to purchase Upton Park, an estate of some thirty acres. Then began an interest that consumed him for the rest of his life – the introduction of plants, seeds and saplings from all over the world, and discovering how to raise and care for them. Through his wide circle of friends and colleagues he obtained plants from China, the West and East Indies, from Russia (even from Siberia), from the Alps, South Africa and West Africa.

One morning, after visiting a ship moored in the Pool of London and arranging for the carriage of boxes and crates of plants, seeds and saplings to Upton Park, he noticed a ship standing isolated in midstream. It was flying the yellow jack, marking the ship as being in quarantine, carrying yellow fever victims. As he watched, a small boat with kegs of water and food supplies was slowly rowed to the ship and the goods rapidly hauled aboard. John Fothergill would not have been slow to ask questions and soon he was deep in conversation with the owner of the rowing boat. The man explained to the doctor that they took supplies to the ship every two or three days, often having the grisly task of returning with a body, firmly stitched in sailcloth. The sailors then trundled a cart with the yellow fever victim to the plague burial ground. John Fothergill asked who was tending the sufferers, but was told that no one would go aboard the vessel even though it appeared that the fever had probably run its course. The doctor insisted that the sailor climbed back into the boat to row him out to the ship, where he found the captain ill and being badly cared for by a frightened cabin boy. After assuring himself that the other sailors were not infected, and enlisting the aid of the cabin boy, he started to care for the captain, visiting each day until the man was out of danger. There were no further cases and the captain recovered.

John Fothergill would accept no fee because his own knowledge of yellow fever had been widened. However upon hearing that the ship was bound for Borneo he asked a favour of the captain – a strange request – he asked for two barrels of earth, to be taken from several parts

opposite
Fothergilla major
Anne Dent

Clematis florida,
a detail from the
cartoon for
'Quaker Botanists',
panel D8 of the
Quaker Tapestry

Nerine curvifolia,
a detail from the
cartoon for
'Quaker Botanists',
panel D8 of the
Quaker Tapestry

of the island. The captain duly returned with the barrels, and John Fothergill spread the earth on a mound of sterilised soil in one of his stove houses. He then watched the curious plants develop, some of which were subsequently successfully transplanted into English gardens or greenhouses, whilst others went to Kew Gardens.

Through Peter Collinson, John Fothergill enjoyed the friendship of John Bartram and his son William Bartram from Pennsylvania, and he received many plants and seeds from both, successfully propagating them at Upton Park and later at Lea Hall in Cheshire. His team of enthusiastic gardeners was skilled in the propagation of plants and always willing to experiment – they had the aid of the cold greenhouse, of glasshouses with heated pipes at the back, and dry stoves that had heated pipes in the floor, as well as bark stoves – large pits filled with tanners' bark that had a similar effect to that of a compost heap in generating heat. John Fothergill paid the expenses of several plant hunters, but also persuaded his friends to join the search. He enlisted the help of the many Quakers who had set up as nurserymen at this time and who were skilled in the germination of seeds and the propagation of plants.

John Fothergill's garden at Upton became a centre for botanists and plantsmen from all over the world, second only to Kew Gardens. William Aiton was the author of *Hortus Kewensis* from which publication we find that John Fothergill and Dr William Pitcairn, a medical colleague, collaborated to send the plant hunter Thomas Blaikie to bring back seeds and plants from the Alps. These included glacier crowfoot (*Ranunculus glacialis*) and bellflower (*Campanula cenisia*), both now difficult to find in nurseries. Also alpine plants *Trifolium alpinum* and *Veronica bellidioides*, and pennycress (*Thlaspi alpinum*), introduced in 1775, were some of the first plants in the Upton Park garden.

John's sister Ann, who looked after him, would urge him to take more rest and so, partly because he also felt the need for more ground, John Fothergill bought Lea Hall in Cheshire. It was here that, in his later years, he would spend time each summer writing on botany, politics, medical matters, and the concerns of the Religious Society of Friends. The needs of the poorer folk in the neighbourhood led John Fothergill to rent two rooms in the White Bear Inn at Middlewich where, for several years, he ran a weekly free clinic during part of his vacation.

John Fothergill's gardens were probably richest in plants from the New World, many received from the indefatigable Bartrams. John Bartram sent a *Magnolia grandiflora*, which flourished at Upton Park, but he had only limited success with the Great Water Lily (*Nelumbo lutea*) sometimes called 'The American Lotus'. John Bartram wrote: 'The creamy-yellow flowers ten to twelve inches across, the circular leaves about two feet in diameter are a sight to behold.' (Fox, 1919:195)

Another of John Fothergill's treasures was the purple or tree anise (*Illicium floridanum*) found in the swamps of Florida and raised from seed by John Ellis (c1710–1776), a member of the Royal Society and a close associate of the group of Quaker plant collectors. It was the only such plant to bloom in Europe and John Fothergill sent a specimen to Linnaeus. A medical colleague sent from the mountains of Aleppo seeds of the *Arbutus andrachne*, a sort of strawberry tree. This grew to a height of twelve feet at Upton and after John Fothergill's death was sold to a nurseryman friend (so that it could be cut into scions for grafting) for £53 11 shillings, a great sum for a plant at that time.

Many of the present clematis have been bred from *Clematis florida* (left) which John Fothergill imported from Japan. There is a specimen of this clematis in the Quaker garden attached to the meeting house in Kendal, although in our eyes today it is far from noteworthy. From China came Lady Tankerville's Bletia, probably the first orchid to flower in England. Also from China came the crab-apple tree (*Malus spectabilis*), which is one of the welcome signs of spring with its pink buds and white flowers. A grander species of orchid *Phaius wallichii* came from India, whilst from the Bartrams in America came the golden amaryllis (*Nerine curvifolia*, left), often known as 'Fothergill's lily'. These two plant hunters also sent *Oenothera biennis*, a large-flowered evening primrose, as well as *Penstemon angustifolius* and a coreopsis, and a phlox (right). The phlox they sent were the forerunners of many of the phlox grown today.

At least two of John Fothergill's introductions are amongst the earliest illustrated flower plates reproduced in Curtis's *The Botanical Magazine*, one being the green ixia (*Ixia viridiflora*). The Swedish plant hunter Carl Peter Thunberg (who had been a pupil of Linnaeus at Uppsala University) discovered it in South Africa, but John Fothergill successfully raised it as a pot plant and saved it from extinction. The corms were regularly eaten as part of the diet of the natives, which no doubt made it even more rare. It is still a protected plant in the wild.

Another illustrated plate was *Calceolaria fothergillii*, an alpine species sometimes called 'Fothergill's slipperwort'. The name of the genus comes from the Greek word meaning shoe. Coming as it did from the inhospitable, storm-racked islands of the Falklands, it is not surprising that collectors and nurserymen in our temperate climate found great difficulty in keeping it alive, but again, John Fothergill found a way to cultivate it. Many plants were sent for interest and classification to Linnaeus, who named a genus of hardy deciduous shrubs after John Fothergill, *Fothergilla* (p.33). These are closely related to the witch hazels, the twigs of that small tree being used in the New World for water divining, and so named because of their seemingly magical powers.

Sometimes in their search for a particular plant the collectors became almost obsessive. John Fothergill had a longing to raise a flowering tea-tree. A director of the East India Company had two tea-trees in his garden at Enfield bearing one white flower annually and seen by Peter Collinson in 1742. These specimens died, however. Linnaeus had one in 1762 that failed to flower, but John Ellis managed to raise a tree from seed and he presented it to Kew Gardens. John Fothergill finally obtained some tea-tree plants from China. Queen Charlotte heard of this and went personally to Upton Park to beg one for her garden. In 1774 a 5ft tall tea-tree flowered at Upton with such success that John Fothergill was able to send specimens from his own garden to the southern provinces of America.

John Fothergill had an aim to introduce useful plants to countries with similar climates where they might flourish. He took bamboo cane and the cinnamon tree from China and helped to establish these in the West Indies, and also proposed the introduction of breadfruit into America. However the War of Independence intervened and it is not until after his death that we hear of the transport of breadfruit again, on the ill-fated *Bounty*, when Captain Bligh hoped to take the plants from Tahiti to the West Indies. A second ship with a consignment made a successful voyage under Captain Bligh some years later.

Ginseng (*Panax pseudoginseng* or *P. ginseng*) had long been valued in China as a remedy for many ailments. John Fothergill was interested to experiment with the plant and found it to be helpful in cases of chronic catarrh and ageing diseases. Peter Collinson imported American ginseng (*Panax quinquefolius*) from Pennsylvania in 1740, and it bloomed happily in his Peckham garden.

In addition to the importation of living plants and seeds to this country, plants were often dried. John Fothergill gave many of them to Joseph Banks and they can be seen in the British Museum Herbarium. While entertaining his friends after Meeting one Sunday a visitor, enjoying the flowers and the foliage in the garden, regretted that the beauty of many plants is fleeting and that it is possible to miss them entirely. John Fothergill agreed and then explained that he was already trying to remedy the situation somewhat by commissioning three or four artists to make botanical drawings and paintings of the plants in Upton Park and Lea Gardens.

After the death of John Fothergill his great friend and colleague John Coakley Lettsom bought the hothouses and most of the hothouse plants from John Fothergill's garden at Upton Park. He then drew up a complete list of the plants and published it as *Hortus Uptoniensis* – this list contained no fewer than 68 species of mesembryanthemum alone.

The house at Upton was enlarged and renamed Ham House and was bought by Samuel Gurney, a brother of Elizabeth Fry. Gurney looked after the gardens and the Park and on his death presented them to the community to become West Ham Park, a valued open space of some eighty acres, where a few of John Fothergill's original plantings still survive. A ginkgo or maidenhair tree (*Ginkgo biloba*) has a trunk six feet in girth at its base. There are a few ancient oaks and yew trees, a medlar and a large plane tree from China introduced by Peter Collinson in 1751 and also a Turkish hazel (*Corylus colurna*). These are but a very small part of the legacy that John Fothergill bequeathed to the gardens of Great Britain.

Phlox paniculata, a detail from the cartoon for 'Quaker Botanists', panel D8 of the Quaker Tapestry

THE VOLATILE CREOLE

In 1767 slavery was a cause for great concern amongst Quakers on both sides of the Atlantic, and the anti-slavery movement was gaining momentum. JOHN COAKLEY LETTSOM (1744–1815) returned from Settle in England, where he had been sent for his education and training as an apothecary. He was heir to a sugar plantation on the small island of Tortola in the West Indies, and to a cotton plantation on the neighbouring island Little Vandyke, and he had come to take up his inheritance. Within a very short space of time we see him presiding over a jubilant crowd of some fifty working slaves and their families, as he gave the slaves their freedom.

right
John Coakley Lettsom

The incredulous neighbouring plantation owners insisted that no man could run a plantation successfully without the use of slave labour. They were full of foreboding, predicting that the slaves would spend their wages on drink, find no employment and become lawless. Many were openly hostile to John Coakley Lettsom, fearing that such an example could signal the end of their way of life. He wrote to his friends in London that he could no longer withhold from the slaves the natural privilege of freedom which Heaven had conferred upon him. Quakers hold a firm belief that there is that of God in every one; as early as 1676 George Fox declared that 'Christ died for the Tawnies and the Blacks as well as for you that are called Whites' (Nickalls, 1975:11) and, in advocating liberty for the slaves, also said 'when they go, and are made free, let them not go away empty-handed'. (Nickalls, 1975:16) John Coakley Lettsom did indeed lose a lot of money by his actions, but he never regretted it, rejoicing in the many small gifts he received over many years from his freed slaves – sweetmeats, shells, hand-made baskets.

However even his disapproving neighbours welcomed his decision to set up the first medical practice on the islands where he trained and employed several ex-slaves to help. It is said that he worked very hard, often seeing fifty patients before breakfast! He seems to have recouped much of his lost income in this way, and when he returned to London he divided the money between himself and his widowed mother, leaving a young woman, an ex-slave, to care for her.

Back in London his old friends and colleagues welcomed John Coakley Lettsom. They had missed the exuberance of the volatile Creole, as he called himself, as well as his enthusiastic support for the many and varied social and scientific interests in which many of them were involved.

John Fothergill, his early mentor, was one of the first to welcome home the returning friend. Knowing the potential of his protégé, John Fothergill advised him to take further training, and John Coakley Lettsom promptly enrolled at Edinburgh University, then went on to the University of Leyden in Holland, gaining an M.D. before starting a practice in London. He involved himself once again in his many outside interests, one of which was natural history and botany in particular, in the enthusiastic company of his Quaker friends, namely John Fothergill, Peter Collinson (now an old man), William Curtis and James Lee, together with non-Quaker friends including Sir Hans Sloane, Philip Miller and Linnaeus. These men, knowledgeable botanists, dedicated gardeners and collectors, formed a circle of influential horticultural expertise for over a century.

The dedication to the second edition of Curtis's *Hortus Londinensis* is to 'John Coakley Lettsom M.D., The Friend of Humanity, The Patron of Science', for it was John Coakley Lettsom who gave financial support to William Curtis as he struggled to make his great contributions to botanical literature. Writing about John Coakley Lettsom's generous nature in a book entitled *Gleanings* the author, Samuel Pratt, had found that John Coakley Lettsom's patients, in times of hardship and illness, might open an envelope containing the prescription and find money as well. It was only then that they understood the cryptic remark made as the doctor left the house, 'the prescription will do thee good'. Pratt describes in great detail a story of John Coakley Lettsom leaving London to travel to Wales to attend an elderly gentleman friend in very poor health. He stayed with this friend for three weeks, until he was sure of the friend's recovery, and on leaving left a box containing further supplies of the necessary medicines, and a cheque. (Pratt, 1802:179/190)

The two doctors, John Fothergill and John Coakley Lettsom, were very different in character, but very much alike in having a large practice, a great concern for all their patients, rich and poor alike, very wide interests, a dedication to the spirit of Quakerism and an unquenchable capacity for hard work. John Coakley Lettsom took a keen interest in the growing of food plants, and many acres of mangel-wurzel are the results of this interest. He also introduced Turkey rhubarb to America and we know, through the letters of Peter Collinson and John Bartram, that the American botanist asked for a recipe for rhubarb tart, so we can assume that Bartram was one of the first to cultivate the plant.

John Coakley Lettsom published many books, pamphlets and papers, on matters medical as well as horticultural, and in 1773 was elected a Fellow of the Royal Society. In his garden at Camberwell, the home where he lived happily for many years with his Quaker wife Ann, he cultivated rare and new plants, many of them acquired through John Fothergill, Peter Collinson and William Curtis, although he also had a plant collector working for him in the Americas and joined syndicates employing these adventurers in other parts of the world.

John Coakley Lettsom had the experience of going to the Pool of London to claim from the customs a consignment of plants and seeds from around the world, and having the disappointment of seeing for himself the rotting stumps of dying plants and putrid seeds ruined by the voyage. He and John Fothergill drew up 'Some directions for taking up plants and shrubs and conveying them by sea'. This included instructions to sea captains, who were advised to give over part of the Great Cabin to the boxes of plants, advice probably not well received by the long-suffering captains in cramped conditions on board ship. John Coakley Lettsom wrote a series of *Hints*, ranging from 'Crime and Punishment; the treatment of debtors', 'Schools for the Poor', 'The (social) treatment of the Deaf and Dumb', 'How to set up a Bee Society' and 'The treatment of Female Servants' – his interests

were wide. In 1770 he wrote a paper on the virtues of tea, a drink whose merits and de-merits were hotly discussed at that time. One of his most valuable writings for us today was his biography of John Fothergill, which was accurate and comprehensive and became the standard work.

John Coakley Lettsom was forever busy. 'I dine with my wife once a week', he wrote (Fox, 1919:109), for, like John Fothergill, he was also a social reformer. He knew the poor, worked for them and amongst them, knew their living conditions and their illnesses – many a direct result of their poverty and squalor – and he ached to be able to help.

We know that for many years John Coakley Lettsom spent his holidays on the sea front at Margate with the children he had sent to the Royal Sea Bathing Hospital. He strongly believed in the beneficial effects of sea bathing, having set up the hospital for 'the scrofulous children of London' (scrofula being a tuberculosis of the lymph nodes, characterised by running sores in the neck region). Although a most unusual way to take a holiday break, he was regularly seen encouraging the children into the sea, enticing them with the prospect of hot soup if they braved the chilly wind and waves.

John Coakley Lettsom brought forty children at a time out of the London slums. He enjoyed watching them savouring the good food and fresh air, playing on the beach, sleeping in warm beds and experiencing the care and concern which few had been able to enjoy in the appalling conditions and overcrowding they were used to. And, of course, the youngsters returned to London in much better health, mentally and physically. Whether this was because of the twice-daily sea bathing or the care, good food, new surroundings and experiences, it matters not. The Royal Sea Bathing Hospital is still on the front at Margate.

In his later years, he tried to spend more time at his home with his wife Ann and in his garden where he continued to grow plants, identifying and carefully labelling them. He invited his many friends to enjoy the murmuring of the bees from the 64 hives he kept amongst the flowers, each hive named after a different nation.

As is true of many Quakers of that era, we read of his life and achievements, his far-sightedness and his innovations, from the Royal Sea Bathing Hospital and his many social concerns, to the setting up of the Medical Society of London on a new representative basis. We also read of his continued interest in natural history and its practical application in his own garden and in the growing collections of that time, and we marvel at his indefatigable industry. Indeed, one of his friends wondered why John Coakley Lettsom never proposed an Act of Parliament, decreeing that each day should contain 48 hours.

John Coakley Lettsom died in 1815, still working as a physician and after visiting a patient only days before his death, despite his own illness. Notwithstanding this, he said that he was content. The genus *Lettsomia* was named after him in recognition of his services to natural history.

THE TRANSPORTATION OF SEEDS, PLANTS AND TREES

For those of us who sometimes find it difficult to keep indoor (and some outdoor) plants alive and flourishing, it is intriguing to think of the immense problems faced by plant hunters to keep their seeds and plants viable when faced by the difficulties not only of circumstance, but also of time.

In addition to the many weeks that could elapse from the time they first lifted the plant or gathered the seed, the plant hunters knew that their finds faced various hazards. Many succumbed during the subsequent voyage in the sailing ships, which could involve two or three months of harsh winds, waves and salt-laden air. Conditions below decks were often fetid; the plants were subjected to depredation from rats, mice and insects and even the unwelcome attentions of the ship's cats! On one occasion a ship lay becalmed in the English Channel for almost a month – so near and yet so far, and a consignment of plants sent by John Bartram to Peter Collinson was captured by French or Spanish privateers in 1745. With Quakerly tolerance John Bartram wrote to Peter Collinson:

> If I could know that [the plants] fell into the hands of men of learning and curiosity I should be more easy. Though they are what is commonly called our enemies, yet, if they make proper use of what I have laboured for, let them enjoy it with the blessing of God. (Darlington, 1849:353)

By far the greatest hazards were the conditions on board ship once the plant hunters had delivered their booty into the care of the captains. Individual plant hunters and collectors tried various methods of preserving the precious cargo, as we have already seen when Peter Collinson writes to advise John Bartram, but three men actually experimented and wrote detailed instructions with illustrations. One was John Ellis, a nurseryman with a well-deserved reputation for germinating seeds, propagating and nurturing strange new plants; the other two were John Fothergill and John Coakley Lettsom. These instructions were to be given to the plant hunters and the captains of the ships carrying their treasures.

In the instructions they stress that plant hunters must be aware of the seeds: 'They must be plump, white and moist, and some cut across and examined with a magnifying glass.' They are warned about seeds sent from China: 'There is reason to suspect that more seeds from China miscarry from the art and treachery of the natives than from the distance, or any defect in conveying them, as many seeds are brought over which appear to have been roasted by the Chinese previous to disposing of them, in order to prevent their vegetation and thereby keep up the demand.'

John Ellis experimented patiently with several methods of preserving seeds and nuts on a long voyage, and John Fothergill and John Coakley Lettsom described some of the methods with further safeguards, for example that seeds, carefully selected, 'may be preserved by rolling each in a coat of yellow beeswax, about half an inch thick; and afterwards a number of these, thus prepared, may be put into a chip-box, which is to be filled with melted beeswax, not made too hot; the outside of the box may then be washed with the sublimate solution and kept during the passage in a cool, airy place.' Similar detailed instructions were given for seeds of various sizes, all to be treated differently.

Plants were to have very special consideration, having carefully balled earth moulded round the roots, then surrounded by damp moss and tied with pack string. After this, they could be placed in specially constructed kegs or wooden boxes with hoops, over which could be thrown canvas as protection from the ship's cats or salt spray. Directions are given about the precise construction of the boxes, with detailed measurements, following complaints by the seamen about earlier boxes being too large and heavy. It was suggested that camphor or small pieces of glass scattered on the surface might help to deter rats and mice.

The instructions to the hard-pressed captains are very demanding: 'The captain who takes charge of them must be particularly informed. He must not keep them always shut up during the voyage; for if he does they will mould and perish by the stagnation of the air, under the covers; and if at any time, by accident or necessity, they should have been exposed to the wind when the waves have white caps, he must be desired to water them well with fresh water, sprinkling all the leaves with it to wash off the salt-drops which may cover them. If it be convenient to the captain to give up a small part of the Great Cabin to the plants, this is certainly by far the best station for them; nor are they much in the way as the place that suits them is close to the stern window. In this case they need not be furnished with their canvas covers; and they may frequently have air, by opening the windows when the weather is quite moderate'.

It is to be hoped that the captain was a keen gardener himself! There is even a list of captains who were sympathetic to the transport of plants. However, all must have been delighted when the invention of the Wardian case (a glass case, like a miniature greenhouse, invented by Nathaniel Ward for protecting plants in transit) made many of the precautions unnecessary.

Peter Collinson, John Fothergill, John Coakley Lettsom, William Curtis, James Lee and James Maddock were some of the Quaker collectors who financed and sent out plant hunters to all parts of the globe. They corresponded with the plant hunters and welcomed the travellers into their homes whenever they were in England, exchanging information and advice. The suggestions which Peter Collinson gave to John Bartram about planting in ox-bladders and making lightweight basket panniers for the packets of seeds made perfect sense, when all the plant hunters had were one or two packhorses or mules. They would have to carry the necessities of life – food, weapons, tools, rods and lines, tarpaulins and blankets, as well as provision for carrying the precious plants, seeds and seedlings.

Many plant hunters travelled alone, although a few would have had a local guide. They would be absent in the wild for months at a time, with instructions to find certain plants and a free hand to collect any plant unknown to them. A good plant hunter was also a good botanist and usually tried to identify the strange plants with local names, as well as attempting to classify the plant botanically.

We remember that John Fothergill asked simply for two barrels of earth when a sea-captain friend made a voyage to Borneo, with interesting results when the contents were spread out in his hothouse to allow the seeds to germinate. This method, however, was usually denied to plant hunters because of the weight. But in spite of all the hazards, successes and failures, the seeds and plants kept arriving from all over the globe to amaze and to delight the gardeners and collectors and to help to foster that climate of co-operation which is one of the pleasures of gardening.

In the New World

LOOKING UP TO NATURE'S GOD

Two dedicated and renowned botanists who made plant hunting their chief concern were John Bartram and William Bartram, father and son.

Peter Collinson's enthusiasm for plants was well known amongst his friends and business acquaintances, especially those that travelled abroad. He would pester them to bring back seeds and plants until eventually the name of JOHN BARTRAM (1699–1777) was suggested as one who would plant hunt for him. It was pointed out that Bartram, twice married and with eleven children, could benefit from the arrangement. Thus at one stroke Peter Collinson's travelling friends were released from Peter's constant, if friendly, demands although they could not have foreseen how vital and productive was the link they helped to forge. At the same time it provided a good living for the American Quaker, and it gave John Bartram the opportunity to move further into the area he loved – botany.

Bartram was a Pennsylvanian farmer and botanist who had mastered Latin in order to understand and use the Linnaean system of plant classification. His farm on the banks of the Schuylkill River had been enlarged by careful drainage and reclamation work. It was here that he made a botanic garden, the first in the New World. The garden and the house (which he built himself out of stone) are now preserved. John Bartram is celebrated as the first American self-taught botanist, a man of great intellect who enjoyed the conversation and company of scientific innovators of the day, yet remained a quiet and rather shy man.

His son WILLIAM BARTRAM wrote that his father's interest in botany began when he rested under a tree during a break from strenuous ploughing. He examined the structure of a flower – in one report, a daisy, in another, a violet. Whichever it was, it fired him with a determination to study, and everything he learned confirmed him in his faith, for he saw God through nature's eye – perfection,

John Bartram
by Robert Pyle

intricacy, and sheer beauty. Written above his greenhouse shed in the botanic garden are the words:

Slave to no sect, who takes no private road,
But looks through nature up to nature's God

Within two years there was a thriving involvement as Peter Collinson inaugurated and organised the box scheme. The original recipients, as we know, included Lord Petre and the Dukes of Norfolk, Richmond and Bedford. A little later, there was Philip Miller of the Chelsea Physic Garden, and also Kew

opposite
Wisteria sinensis
Audrey Jennett

41

Gardens under the patronage and with the personal interest of the Princess of Wales.

In addition to plants, John Bartram sent maps, shells, minerals, fossils and drawings to Peter Collinson. As we read earlier, in October 1737 he sent the fifteen turtle eggs that hatched out on the day that they were collected from the ship, to Peter Collinson's great delight. Eighteen years later John Bartram was still sending gifts that he knew would interest and intrigue his friend. He sent a live Great Mud Turtle, often called a snapping turtle from its habit of lying at the bottom of a lake, head protruding from the mud, to catch fishes and ducks. In its turn it was 'much hunted for, to feast our gentry withal'. (Cruickshank, 1957:83) Peter Collinson installed it in his pond where it ate all his fish! In return Peter Collinson sent lengths of material, magnifying glasses, a pocket compass with a dial to it to tell the time, books, tools, letters of introduction for his expeditions and advice on the transport of seeds and plants ... and how to make a rhubarb tart! John Coakley Lettsom, as we have already read, had just introduced Turkey rhubarb to America.

John Bartram was delighted to receive an engraved silver cup from Sir Hans Sloane, and from Philip Miller came seeds that included plums, nectarines and apricots for John Bartram's own garden. Miller and Bartram corresponded from 1755, both regretting that their correspondence had not begun earlier, for they had knowledge to exchange to their mutual benefit. In his *Gardeners' dictionary*, Miller credits John Bartram with the *Lilium philadelphicum* (left), *Toxicodendron serrata* (now *Rhus toxicodendron* or *R. radicans*, poison ivy or poison oak), *Magnolia acuminata*, *Veratrum americanum* and others. However John Hendley Barnhart, in his study on the significance of John Bartram's work to botany and horticulture, states that a large proportion of plants credited as introductions to Philip Miller were also discovered by John Bartram. If this is true, John Bartram was probably responsible for the first appearance in Britain of between 150 and 200 new plants. It should be remembered, however, that the success of these introductions depended not only on the discovery and transportation of plants and seeds but also on the care and expertise lavished on them by the recipients.

Eventually, as a result of Peter Collinson's habit of reading to the Fellows of the Royal Society many of John Bartram's letters, the award of £50 yearly and the post of 'King's Botanist' was made to John Bartram in 1765. Dr Solander, who travelled with Cook to New Zealand, named the genus *Bartramia* after

him, and made lists of the plants which John Bartram, as King's Botanist, had sent to King George III. In all Bartram gathered 308 specimens during his travels through Georgia, Carolina and East Florida. Dr Solander and John Ellis were very excited when Bartram sent the first Venus flytrap (*Dionaea muscipula*, right); they made drawings and detailed descriptions of this new and curious plant.

Bartram's journeyings began with short expeditions along the Schuylkill River, in the months when the work demands of his farm were not so heavy. Peter Collinson warned John Bartram not to allow his passion for botany to close his eyes to the basic necessity of attending to his farm, but as his family responsibilities eased and as Peter Collinson found more subscribers for the boxes, John Bartram was able to travel further afield – to Virginia and on to the James River area, where he stayed two nights in Williamsburg before crossing the Appalachian mountains. He returned home laden with many new seeds and plants. Many of his expeditions he made alone, facing dangers from wild animals and reptiles, reporting an encounter with a nest of rattle snakes and being frightened by a hostile Indian, who menacingly ate the brim of his hat! The Indians had a name for him – Pug-Puggy, which translates as the flower gatherer, but they admired the way he faced the challenges of just keeping alive in a largely unexplored terrain.

During these first explorations John Bartram collected *Rhododendron calendulaceum*, a brilliant orange-red azalea, parent of many hybrids, which was lost after the initial cultivation but rediscovered in 1806. Another rhododendron (*Rhododendron maximum*) was the first really large species sent to Britain. Two other shrubs, the Calico Bush (*Kalmia latifolia*) and Sheep Laurel (*Kalmia angustifolia*) were sent during this period. A bulb of the wood lily (*Lilium philadelphicum*) was another introduction which was lost and found – sent to Europe in 1675, lost to cultivation, rediscovered by John Bartram and sent to Philip Miller at Chelsea in 1737. *Lilium superbum*, a very colourful lily, easily grown and still very popular, also dates from this time.

In 1743 John Bartram elected to travel with the interpreter Conrad Weiser, who was to attend a conference between the Indians and the colonists near Syracuse. The journey north took four weeks, during which Bartram discovered a tree growing 100 feet high, the *Magnolia acuminata*. Twenty years later Peter Collinson wrote, 'I am in high delight, my two mountain magnolias are pyramids of flowers'.

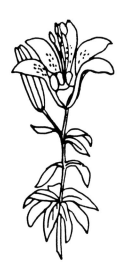

Lilium philadelphicum, a detail from the cartoon for 'Quaker Botanists', panel D8 of the Quaker Tapestry

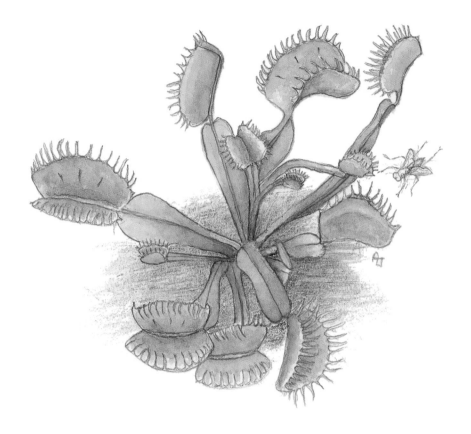

John Bartram kept a journal of this expedition and sent three copies to Peter Collinson. Two copies were stolen in a pirate raid on the ship carrying them, but the third arrived safely. So many people in London were asking to read it that in 1751 Peter Collinson had the journal published, under John Bartram's name and entitled *Observations on the Inhabitants, Climate, Soil, Rivers, Productions, Animals made on his Travels from Pennsylvania in Onondago, Oswego, and the Lake Ontario.* Peter Collinson's own copy with his manuscript notes is in the British Museum Herbarium.

Ten years later John Bartram is accompanied by 'my little botanist' (Darlington, 1849:193), William, his fifteen-year-old son, who then made other journeys with his father. In the first half of the 1760s they undertook several journeys, staying with Dr Gardens, a famous botanist introduced by Peter Collinson. His name is remembered in the fragrant *Gardenia.* During this time John Bartram met Martha

Logan, one of the few women botanists on record, who sent him seeds and plants. Later, he was badly hurt falling from a tree whilst collecting seeds but he still travelled to Pittsburg where he records finding pecans, and in 1762 he travelled extensively along the 600-mile valley of the Shenandoah River.

A year later John Bartram wrote to Peter Collinson that he longed to travel the course of the Ohio and Mississippi Rivers and into Florida. At the age of sixty-six this ambition was realised, although he suffered severe seasickness and stayed in Charleston with his friend Dr Gardens who cared for him until he was fit to continue his travels. He then went on to explore four or five hundred miles with his son William Bartram, map-making and plant hunting.

In the valley of the Altamara River he made two of his most significant discoveries, *Nyssa ogeche* and the beautiful *Franklinia alatamaha,* named by John Bartram after his friend Benjamin Franklin. This tree, growing twenty

above
Dionaea muscipula
Audrey Jennett

43

feet high with white, saucer shaped flowers from late summer to late autumn, was lost in the wild, the supposition being that the small stand of trees had been washed away in a flood or similar natural disaster. Strangely, John Bartram does not appear to have gathered any propagation material on that occasion although he recognised the botanical importance of the find. It is possibly explained by the fact that he suffered a severe attack of malaria. 'I am so very weke I can hardly stand', he says in one of his letters. (Darlington, 1849:281)

It was William Bartram in 1773 and again in 1777 who rediscovered the small swampy area where these trees were growing and brought back seeds and cuttings. We know that he gave seeds to his father for their own garden, and that in 1773 he sent some to John Fothergill, who successfully germinated some of the seeds and presented seedlings to Kew Gardens. A few enthusiastic collectors in England grew the trees, although the climate did not encourage full growth of flowers or fruit. It is thought that Humphry and Moses Marshall provided these keen growers with the seeds and that Moses (in 1790) and Scots gardener John Lyon (in 1803) were the last people to see *Franklinia alatamaha* in the wild. However many of these trees now flourish in America, all thought to be the descendants of the rarity discovered by John Bartram and collected by William Bartram and Humphry and Moses Marshall.

John Bartram's great contribution to science in the New World was recognised by his contemporaries, and his name can be seen as the second of the signatories as a founder member of the American Philosophical Society, after the name of Benjamin Franklin. Linnaeus stated that John Bartram was 'the greatest of natural botanists' and he was elected to the Royal Academy of Sciences in Stockholm.

John Bartram's garden on the Schuylkill River is now a park in the city of Philadelphia, under the devoted care of the John Bartram Association. In Britain we remember his great contribution to our gardens when we see *Rhododendron maximum* and *Rhododendron periclymenoides*, *Iris cristata*, *Phlox divaricata* (opposite), *Phlox maculata* and *Phlox subulata*, the bergamot (*Monarda didyma* - left) the climbing Dutchman's pipe (*Aristolochia macrophylla*) and so many others blooming in beauty today.

William Bartram was indeed an excellent botanist and a talented illustrator. The Duchess of Portland, dining one day with Peter Collinson, was shown some of William's botanical drawings that John had sent to his old friend. She promptly offered William,

through Peter Collinson, twenty guineas to make her more drawings, and promised more employment through her wide circle of gardening and botanically minded friends. Peter Collinson also showed the illustrations to John Fothergill, who commissioned William to make drawings of shells, tortoises and turtles, at all stages of development and with notes and observations.

John Fothergill, in 1772, tried to give William Bartram further encouragement by agreeing to fund a journey of exploration into East and West Florida. It was then largely unexplored territory, many parts occupied only by native peoples (Red Indians to William). Through a medical friend of John Fothergill, William Bartram was to receive £50 yearly for two years, be well-equipped at John Fothergill's expense and be reimbursed for all packing and forwarding costs, in return for new seeds and plants, and drawings of birds, animals, reptiles and insects made en route.

The two years came and went and still William Bartram went on with the exploration. He travelled the coastlines of the Carolinas and of Georgia, into Florida; then westward to Apalachee Bay and Lower Georgia, later crossing the mountains of Tennessee and travelling through Chactaw and Cherokee Indian territory into present day Alabama. However, John Fothergill received little in return for his investment! The beginning of the War of Independence hampered the dispatch of letters and goods, even on the few occasions when William Bartram reached civilisation. But much of the paucity of drawings and specimens was due to the fact that William Bartram was a wanderer rather than a determined explorer. Given up for lost several times, he was thought to have been killed by hostile tribes or to have succumbed to the many dangers in a largely unexplored country. He travelled mostly on foot, saved by his gentle friendliness towards everyone he met, and by his undoubted survival skills learned from his father. About six years later he returned to Philadelphia to find that his father had died and the War of Independence was engulfing the country.

Thirteen years later William Bartram wrote the book *Travels through North and South Carolina, Georgia, East and West Florida, etc*, twice reprinted in England and translated into French. His obvious delight in every aspect of nature breaks through the somewhat florid style of writing of the time. He recounts his adventures through a hostile, testing environment – both his encounters with natural dangers and in his meetings with various Indian tribes:

Monarda didyma, a detail from the cartoon for 'Quaker Botanists', panel D8 of the Quaker Tapestry

opposite
Phlox divaricata
Anne Dent

I drew up my light vessel on the sloping shore, that she might be safe in case of a sudden storm of wind in the night, A few yards back the land was a little elevated and overgrown with shrubs and low trees, . . . yet sufficiently high to shelter me from the chilling dews; and here . . . I fixed my encampment. A brisk wind arising from the lake drove away the clouds of mosquitoes into the thickets. I now, with difficulty and industry, collected a sufficiency of dry wood to keep up a light all night, and to roast some trout which I had caught when descending the river; their heads I stewed in the juice of oranges, which, with boiled rice, afforded me a wholesome and delicious supper; I hung the remainder of my broiled fish on the snags of some shrubs over my head. At last, I spread my skins and blanket upon the clean sands by my fire side, and betook myself to repose.

At midnight I awake; when, raising my head erect, I find myself alone in the wilderness of Florida, on the shores of Lake George. . . When quite awake, I start at the heavy tread of some animal; the dry limbs of trees upon the ground crackle under his feet; the close, shrubby thickets part and bend under him as he rushes off.

I rekindle my sleepy fire, . . . the bright flames ascend and illuminate the ground and groves around me. Looking up I find my fish carried off, though I thought them safe on the shrubs above my head, but their scent was I suppose too powerful an attraction to the rapacious wolf. How much easier it might have been for him to have leaped upon my breast in the dead of sleep, and torn my throat, than to have made protracted and circular approaches, then, after espying the fish over my head, with the greatest caution to rear up, and take them off the snags one by one, and that so cunningly as not to awaken me until he had fairly accomplished his purpose. (Bartram, 1791:156/7)

Wild animals and the elements were not the only hazards, however, and William Bartram writes of an encounter with an Indian who was on horseback and armed with a rifle:

On perceiving that he was armed with a rifle, the first sight of him startled me, and I endeavoured to elude his sight by stopping my pace, and keeping large trees between us; but he espied me, and turning short about, set spurs to his horse and came up on full gallop. I never before this was afraid at the sight of an Indian, but at this time I must own that my spirits were much agitated; I saw at once that, being unarmed, I was in his power; and having now but a few moments to prepare, I resigned myself entirely to the will of the Almighty, trusting to his mercies for my preservation; my mind became tranquil and I resolved to meet the dreaded foe with resolution and cheerful confidence. The intrepid Seminole stopped suddenly, three or four yards before me and silently viewed me, his countenance angry and fierce, shifting his rifle from shoulder to shoulder and looking about instantly on all sides. I advanced towards him and with an air of confidence offered my hand, hailing him, Brother, at this he hastily jerked back his arm, with a look of malice, rage, and disdain; when again he looked at me more attentively, he instantly spurred up to me and with dignity in his look and action, gave me his hand. In fine, we shook hands, and parted in a friendly manner; and he informed me of the course and distance to the trading house, where I found he had been extremely ill-treated the day before. (Bartram, 1791:20/21)

William Bartram, upon going to the trading post, heard that the Indian had left there vowing to kill the first white man he met. This was evidently not his only such encounter with native peoples, but he was usually received with guarded courtesy, and then, because of his gentleness, offered friendship and help.

Although being offered a post as Professor of Botany at Philadelphia University, William Bartram refused the honour. He preferred instead to tend his father's garden, identifying, drawing and raising plants, at one with the natural world and his God, and dying a contented old man at the age of eighty-four.

* * *

The seventeenth and eighteenth centuries represented the Golden Age in botany and gardening, and an explosion of new plants entered into our gardens. In those early days, many emigrant Quakers travelled to and from the American colonies and frequently collected seeds and plants. One of the earliest Quakers who had emigrated from Europe and who made a great contribution to the spread of plants and trees was probably JAMES REID (born around 1660, died around 1695), the son of an Irish Quaker. In the first half of the 1680s he was sent to Virginia to collect plants for the King's garden at Hampton Court, thus establishing himself as a plant hunter; he was paid £234 11s 9d for 'collecting in foreign parts'. In 1685 he sailed to Pennsylvania with a cargo of several hundred saplings, seeds and plants, together with garden equipment bought by William Penn for his garden at Pennsbury. Five years later he was sent to Barbados by a syndicate of patrons in England, which included Hans Sloane, John Fothergill and James Lee. Sixty plants, new to Britain, were raised from the seeds he collected on that expedition.

He continued his searches in the Bahamas, and amassed a consignment of 86 trees, shrubs and seeds, and descriptions of 93 plant species. In *Hortus Kewensis* he is credited with the introduction of *Solanum mammosum*, the nipple nightshade or bachelor's pear. He drowned before his prime off the coast of Jamaica.

A number of other Quakers are commemorated by having plants named after them. The genus *Logania* and the natural order *Loganiaeceae* preserve the name of JAMES LOGAN (1674–1751), whom we have already encountered as a rival for the affections of Ann Shippen in the account of Thomas Story. Born in Ireland the son of a Quaker schoolmaster, James Logan received a good education and at the age of twenty-five travelled to Pennsylvania with William Penn, acting as his secretary. As a man of great scholarship and with interest in many things scientific, he was impressed with the work of Linnaeus on plant classification.

Logan experimented with the maize plant, scientifically demonstrating and proving that it was necessary for pollen to be conveyed to the ovary for the production of seed. On the advice of Thomas Story he wrote of his experiments to Peter Collinson, that indefatigable correspondent who encouraged scientific exploration in many fields, and who introduced the treatise, written in Latin by James Logan, to the Royal Society. John Fothergill, another of Logan's correspondents, reprinted this in English, with a preface, in 1747. With these mailings came seeds and plants in both directions over the Atlantic, for Logan was a keen botanist, enjoying the respite from his heavy commitments. He became Secretary to the Colony, Chief Justice, and President of the Council.

Logan made several expeditions into Indian Territory, getting to know, understand and appreciate the American Indian culture. Many of his new plant discoveries were made on these travels. The Indians loved and trusted him and he was present at the signing of the treaties between William Penn and several of the Indian tribes. A panel of the Quaker Tapestry, commemorating one such treaty, is based on Benjamin West's famous painting *Penn's treaty with the Indians* where, it is said, James Logan and Thomas Story are depicted standing to the left of William Penn. There is some debate, however, about the date of the treaty shown in the painting, either 1682 or 1701.

He is remembered today for the bequest of his large library – the Loganian Library – to the city of Philadelphia.

THREE BLASTS OF A HORN

From the time when early man started to cultivate a small patch of earth and grow food, gardeners had always been present. Nurserymen came later when gardeners, who were better than others at propagating and raising plants, started to sell their surplus young plants or seeds – vegetables, herbs and, later, flowers.

One of the earliest Quaker gardeners and nurserymen was HEW WOOD (died 1701), friend of Thomas Story and a leading member of the Society of Friends – he became a Quaker in around 1669 at Glasfoord Meeting on the West Coast of Scotland – and was later a prominent member of Hamilton Meeting near Glasgow. He was clerk to the meeting, a writer on religious subjects, and eventually gave his house to the meeting and left land for a burial ground.

He is recorded as having a flourishing nursery business and later was gardener to the Duke of Hamilton. John Reid, a fellow Quaker and author of *The Scots Gard'ner*, writing about cider apples and pears for perry, recorded that Hew Wood sold 'genetmoil and musts, pipens and parmains, and for Perry, the Bromsbury and ruddy horse-pear'.

But the peaceful gardener was not allowed to enjoy the gentle and satisfying job of raising plants and trees. In 1670 he suffered the first of many imprisonments for his faith. Shouting and the sound of heavy boots on the stairs interrupted the quiet of Yearly Meeting in Edinburgh. Soldiers burst into the room and advanced swiftly towards the elders' bench. The men sitting quietly there, around the clerk's table, did not move. The soldiers, brandishing their muskets, anticipating retaliation or panic, were silenced, unsure of their next move. The sergeant moved forward, obviously with orders to arrest the ringleaders of this subversive group of Quakers. Again quietly, the clerk of the meeting and the elders were herded towards the door, en route for prison. Hew Wood was amongst the twenty Quakers arrested that day, and over the next thirty years the arrests continued and he was subjected to violence and abuse at the hands of the Covenanters and Presbyterians.

Just before his death in 1701, we find Hew Wood reporting to yearly meeting 'that ther was one charg of horning' against him for non-payment of tithes, which charge the Duchess of Hamilton refused to accept, probably because she didn't want to lose a good gardener! The term horning is explained by Sir Walter Scott in *The Antiquary*. No man could be arrested for debt in Scotland. The King would send a royal command to the debtor 'to do him justice' within a certain number of days. If the payment was not forthcoming the man was declared a rebel for disobeying the command of the King. Three blasts of a horn in the Market Place in Edinburgh led to the man's imprisonment as a rebel, not as a debtor.

Hew's eldest son JAMES WOOD (born 1663) followed his father's profession and became gardener to the Duke of Queensbury at Drumlarig Castle. Scottish gardeners were much in demand, especially in London, where we find John Fothergill, William Curtis and James Lee importing gardeners from Scotland.

As the enthusiasm for new plants grew, the special skills of the nurserymen were in demand. Collectors such as Peter Collinson, John Fothergill and John Coakley Lettsom, with their businesses and professions as their main concern, were very thankful for the expertise and dedication of the nurserymen. At one time there were fourteen firms of nurserymen around London and it was often into their care that the seeds and plants, in various stages of viability, were sent when received and sorted from the ships.

When we remember that the gardeners of this period had little direct knowledge of soil or climatic conditions in the countries from which the plants were sent, the results they achieved are all the more remarkable. John Bartram and other plant hunters did indeed often include helpful details of habitat, but in many cases the documents with the information arrived mildewed or chewed by rats; letters sent separately often failed to

opposite
Fuchsia magellanica
Audrey Jennett

49

arrive. We find that some plants which were listed as being introduced by one plant hunter but did not survive, are then later accredited to the person who successfully raised the new plant.

One of the earliest Quakers to be listed as a nurseryman as well as a gardener was WILLIAM MILLER (1655–1743), another Scot; he was born in Hamilton near Glasgow and became a horticulturist. In 1689 he was appointed gardener at the Abbey of Holyrood House – there had been a garden there as early as 1500 on the site of a drained loch. In 1670 part of the garden became the first home of the Physic Garden, later to become the Edinburgh Botanic Garden.

The Millers lived in a house in the King's Garden and their home was frequently used as a meeting place for Quaker committees. William Miller had two sons who both chose horticulture as their career. The eldest son GEORGE MILLER was born in 1682 and succeeded his father as head gardener at Holyrood House, later becoming gardener to the Duke of Hamilton at Kinneil. William's second son, another WILLIAM MILLER (1684–1757) went into business as a seedsman and nurseryman, and when his brother George left for Kinniel he rented the garden at Holyrood, becoming head gardener and continuing his nursery business. He succeeded his father as clerk and treasurer of Edinburgh Meeting, and the house in the King's Garden was also to become a venue for Quaker committees. Obviously the titled folk for whom the Millers worked thought too highly of their horticultural skills to take any notice of the fact that they were Quakers and as such suspected as subversives by the establishment. William's son, yet another WILLIAM and grandson to the first William Miller (Quakers were notoriously economical with names!) succeeded to the post of head gardener and took over the flourishing seed and nursery business. Thus the gardens of Holyrood House were in the care of Quakers for three generations.

Arthur Raistrick, in his book *Quakers in Science and Industry* (1950) connects Philip Miller, Gardener of the Chelsea Physic Garden from 1724 until 1769, with this Scottish family with the same surname. However, we are not able to substantiate such a connection, even though we know that amongst this famous gardener's closest friends were many of the Quaker plant hunters and collectors of that period.

THE HAMPTON COURT VINE

One Quaker who was not a professional gardener or nurseryman, nor had he any forbears who were plantsmen, was JOHN WARNER (1674/5–1760). He was born in Whitechapel, at the sign of the 'Bathing Tub and Milk Pail', where his father was a cooper by trade. John and his elder brother Simeon became merchants at Rotherhithe and John, an enthusiastic gardener, laid out a large garden and stove house. They grew many varieties of fruit trees in the garden, breeding and propagating them (one variety of apple being 'Warner's King' a green cooking apple still grown today), whilst the stove house, containing pineapples and other exotics and hothouse plants, attracted many interested visitors.

In about 1718 John Warner and his wife entertained two visitors from Hamburg – Jacob Hagan, a nurseryman, and his wife (who was John's niece). The German nurseryman was a wine grower and he had brought some bunches of his black dessert grapes which no doubt the family would enjoy with cheese after their meal. The grapes were large and luscious and much appreciated by the Warners. After lunch all four started a tour of the glasshouses and stove houses which John Warner had installed and which were of such interest to the many visitors who enjoyed the variety of unusual plants. Two years later, on their next visit, the Hagans brought some rooted scions, the first 'Black Hamburgh' grapes to be raised in Britain. The vine grew so vigorously that John Warner was able to supply his friends with bunches of the grapes, and, as is so often the way with gardeners, to give away special gifts of cuttings. In 1768 he gave a cutting to Charles Raymond, who lived at Valentines near Wanstead in London. In turn a cutting from this was given to Lancelot 'Capability' Brown who planted it at Hampton Court, and so it became 'The Hampton Court Vine'. This famous vine is now more than 230 years old. It is restricted to bearing 500 to 600 bunches each year at an average weight of twelve ounces. The original vine given to Valentines had a shorter life – in 1908 a new head gardener from Sandringham, unaware of its history, destroyed the vine completely. In 1950, however, a cutting was sent from Hampton Court to Valentines where it again thrives on the wall of the Old English Garden there.

John Warner was an active Quaker, a member of Horsleydown Meeting, which is recorded on the Quaker Tapestry panel

'Keeping the meeting', depicting a meeting house demolished in 1670 by order of the King, under the supervision of Sir Christopher Wren, to prevent Quakers holding their meetings for worship. The panel shows the meeting continuing on the rubble as the building is pulled down around them. A new meeting house, where John Warner attended, was built later.

The practice of gifts of cuttings, seeds and plants being exchanged amongst gardeners continues. A Nottingham Quaker, an enthusiastic and knowledgeable gardener, visited Hampton Court some years ago and chatted about the history of the vine to the vinekeeper, mentioning that he was a Quaker nurseryman himself. He came away with a cutting which subsequently grew, fruited and in turn was given to other friends!

This is one of the glories of plantsmen – their generosity knows no bounds!

THE WALWORTH NURSERIES

The well known Walworth Nurseries were started by Warrington-born JAMES MADDOCK (1715–68). There is no record that any of his family had any horticultural background, and when he was married in 1753 he is described in Quaker records as being a soap-boiler, but obviously his heart and interests were on a different plane. He and his wife moved to the Norfolk area where, we believe, he took some training in horticulture. His son, another JAMES, was born in 1764 near Yarmouth, his birth being recorded in the Quaker records of Norfolk and Norwich Monthly Meeting. A few years later we find that James Maddock the elder had moved to London where, in Walworth, he established a nursery business.

The younger James Maddock lived for some time in South Cave, near Hull, rejoining his family when he was about thirteen; he was probably away at school at the time of the move. By 1777 the Walworth nursery was flourishing, one of the many nurseries growing up in the area to the south of London where there was land available close to their patrons – these were people indulging in the fashionable interest of establishing gardens. They were curious about the new flowers and exotics being brought from overseas and then raised and cultivated by the many nurserymen around the capital.

James Maddock's influential book, *The Florist's Directory, a treatise on the culture of flowers*, was published posthumously by his son in 1822. The meaning of the word florist has changed somewhat. In the eighteenth century it referred to cultivated plants rather than the more specialised connotation today. The two James Maddocks produced numerous new varieties of flowers and their priced lists or catalogues were the first to be issued in London, although it appears to have been a regular practice in the north. The lists show the nursery to have been a vital centre 'well known to the curious in flowers throughout the kingdom'. It was not only flowers, however, which appeared in their lists, gooseberries making an early, if not their first, appearance.

William Curtis, in compiling *The Botanical Magazine*, relied heavily on living specimens raised in the many nurseries around London. The Walworth nursery supplied a large proportion of these, being one of the most regular and valuable sources. The well-known *Narcissus tenuior*, raised by James Maddock, is illustrated in *The Botanical Magazine*, vol. XI, plate 379.

THE LEE FAMILY AND THE VINEYARD NURSERY

The thick mud oozed between the toes of the mudlark, a lad of about twelve years old, as he squelched his way along the edges of the river, his eyes on some thick, brown paper packets floating on the water just beyond his reach. In spite of the cold, he waded into the murky waters of the Thames, gathering as many packets as he could before the tide carried them away. Clutching his booty, he climbed back onto the bank and, running hard, chased the packages that had escaped him, plunging into the river ahead of them. He then set off at a brisk trot along the riverbank, turning into the maze of small streets leading towards Addison Bridge, the present site of Olympia. He was making for the Vineyard Nursery – one of the most famous nurseries in London.

JAMES LEE (1715–95) saw the dripping, shivering boy as he came through the gates and soon had him drying in front of the fire with a steaming bowl of broth and a hunk of bread in his hands. James Lee left the lad enjoying the food and the warmth whilst he carefully separated the brown paper packets and laid them on a table to dry out.

Sam the mudlark had at first wondered why the Quaker had given him the job of watching Philip Miller each time a ship carrying seeds and plants for the Chelsea Physic Garden had docked. James Lee had been apprenticed to Philip Miller some years previously and had seen him gathering up the empty packets after each batch of seeds had been sown, carefully labelled and the greenhouse door locked. Miller then walked through the garden to the river and threw the empty packets into the Thames. Miller, unlike most gardeners, preferred to keep the secrets of his new plants until they were fully grown and he could claim early and exclusive recognition for a new introduction. But, as James Lee explained to Sam, the heavy writing on the labels could often be deciphered if snatched from the water in time. Then James Lee would send a list of these seeds to his plant hunters and hope to raise seedlings to sell in his own nursery, having them early on the market and beating his rivals!

So Sam had a regular job and one in which he was interested. He loved the nursery and would wander round the garden and into the greenhouses looking at the plants, asking questions of the gardeners and envying the garden boys, even those whose job it was to stoke the fires for the stove houses and the greenhouses. These lads worked in shifts, round the clock, shovelling wood and coal every two hours, sleeping above the boiler house, warm and snug. Maybe James Lee, noting the lad's enthusiasm and thirst for knowledge, promoted him. And was it Sam, in his wanderings along the riverside at Wapping, who first spotted the unusual and flamboyant plant flourishing in the tiny window of a seaman's cottage and told James Lee?

James Lee saw the plant *Fuchsia magellanica* (p.48 – one version of the story names it as *Fuchsia coccinea*) and tried to buy it from the seaman's wife. She was very proud of her glorious plant and explained to James Lee that her husband, who had just returned to sea, had brought it for her from his last voyage. The nurseryman complimented the woman on the care she was obviously lavishing on the plant, giving it just the right amount of water and light and deadheading it regularly. She refused to part with it, however, even though James Lee offered her £8, a very large sum of money. James thought that he could see a way that would satisfy them both. The nurseryman explained that if she would sell the plant he could raise many more from it. He would look after the cuttings in his greenhouse and return three well-grown plants before her husband returned. The woman looked at James Lee in his Quaker garb and felt that she could trust this friendly, interesting man and finally said that she would agree to the £8 and the promise of three new plants, if James Lee would also show her how to make new plants. And so the bargain was struck and James Lee walked away with the plant. It is said that he raised well over 100 plants from the cuttings he took which he sold at one guinea each and the seaman's wife received her three plants, plus pots, soil and a demonstration on plant propagation. This was not the first fuchsia to be introduced into England, but the story, recounted in the *Lincoln Herald* some years later, is an example of the way in which new plants were made available to gardeners and enthusiasts all over the country by the efforts of the nurserymen.

James Lee, a Scot, left home in 1732, at the age of seventeen, to walk to London. We know that he contracted smallpox in Lichfield, recovered and we believe took up an apprenticeship with Philip Miller at the Apothecaries Garden in Chelsea, which would account for his wide knowledge of botany. At one time he was associated with the garden at Syon House, and he also worked as head gardener for the Duke of Argyll at Whitton Place, learning of the box trade instigated by Peter Collinson whom he would know from Quaker meetings in London.

In 1760 he went into partnership with Lewis Kennedy. Together they bought a thatched cottage with wine cellars in Hammersmith, once the site of a successful 'Burgundy' wine production, not an unusual trade at that time, so they called their nursery The Vineyard. It became one of the foremost nurseries in the country; indeed, J. C. Loudon, the renowned horticultural writer, declared it to be 'unquestionably the finest nursery in Britain, or rather, the world'. Certainly their trade was worldwide. There are two invoices for roses and other plants to be sent to the gardens of Malmaison in France for the Empress Josephine, totalling £3,300 – and this was during the Napoleonic Wars! There is an account of the furious Napoleon ordering the digging up of all the English roses in Malmaison, and the ravished bushes being replaced in 1811 by Josephine, who was by then divorced from Napoleon.

Many were the visitors welcomed at the Vineyard. Pierre-Joseph Redouté, of rose fame, Joseph Banks, plant hunters, botanists, garden enthusiasts, Quaker friends of James Lee, for whom he raised many difficult seeds and plants sent from abroad. James Lee was one of the Quakers elected to the Royal Society, the first nurseryman to use the Linnaean classification in his catalogues, and one of the founder members of the Linnaean Society.

The Vineyard Nursery is credited with the introduction of 135 new plants to Britain from countries throughout the world. Lee and Kennedy specialised in Australian plants, no doubt due to the friendships between James Lee, Joseph Banks and Sydney Parkinson. They sent out their own plant hunters, including David Burton, who did most of his plant gathering in Australia, the grandson of James Lee. In 1788, the year in which Sydney was founded, the nursery was credited with the introduction of five new Australian species. One of them, *Banksia serrata*, is claimed to be the first plant raised in this country from seeds gathered around Botany Bay. James Lee seems to have made friends with his plant hunters, and they became regular visitors, often staying with the family between their expeditions.

His son, the young James Lee, was a worthy successor to his father, carrying on the nursery, enhancing its reputation but, above all, continuing the friendships enjoyed by his father. There is considerable correspondence from the younger James Lee, remonstrating with Sir J. E. Smith about the treatment of Edward Masson, a plant hunter of great renown who served for 25 years on a pittance and was treated badly by the syndicate that employed him. The Vineyard was indeed in the forefront of botany and the introduction of

new plants, a meeting place for everyone who loved plants, and who appreciated the welcome and hospitality which the Lee family gave so freely.

THE NORTHERN KEW GARDENS

One Yorkshire family of nurserymen, however, remained detached from the London scene, and made their own very individual contribution to the expansion of plants and flowers, not necessarily exotics. This was the BACKHOUSE family.

James Backhouse came from a long line of Quaker businessmen; his father and grandfather were bankers in Darlington. James had had lung trouble when he was young which led him to seek an outdoor life and this in turn developed his love of plants so that botany and horticulture became his chosen career. He trained at a nursery in Norwich and in 1816 bought a well-established nursery business in York, with his brother Thomas Backhouse as partner.

James Backhouse married Deborah Lowe, who bore two children but died after giving birth to their third child, who also died. No doubt this loss contributed to the decision which James made four years later. A staunch member of the Society of Friends, we find him with a companion, GEORGE WASHINGTON WALKER (1800–1859), a draper and a member of Newcastle Monthly Meeting, embarking on a lengthy journey. With the support of London Yearly Meeting they began travelling in the ministry, taking the message of Quakerism to Tasmania (then called Van Diemen's Land) and Australia, encouraging small meetings and setting up new meetings.

They tried to take passage on a convict ship but were refused permission, so they travelled steerage to Van Diemen's Land, carrying letters of introduction to governors of penal colonies and local officials, and reported back to yearly meeting and to Elizabeth Fry. They walked thousands of miles (for horses were scarce) during the years they spent there, becoming welcome guests in homes and settlements, and in early hints of ecumenism were frequently invited to speak in churches. They saw for themselves the conditions in the penal institutions and the treatment of the aboriginal people, visiting every prison and penal colony, even accepting an invitation to spend half an hour on the treadmill. They talked to the prisoners and the governors and reported on the very varied treatments and the success or otherwise of the regimes.

53

There is a story that when James Backhouse and George Walker arrived in one settlement, James was asked for advice on vine culture and he gave freely of his knowledge and expertise. How did he reconcile his desire to help these settlers with his very strong teetotal beliefs, we wonder?

In addition they visited many Quakers who had emigrated and put groups in touch with each other. They travelled for the next nine years, visiting also South Africa and Mauritius.

At Cape Town George Washington Walker and James Backhouse decided to go their separate ways; George Walker felt that it was his calling to return to Tasmania to strengthen the community there. He arrived back there in 1840, and shortly afterwards married Sarah Mather. He was well respected by local Friends, and after his death in 1859 Hobart Town Monthly Meeting sent the testimony to his life and work to London Yearly Meeting.

Throughout his travels James Backhouse, with his butterfly net and botanical reference books, identified and carefully recorded the flora and fauna. He is credited with publishing the first botanical dictionary of Australian plants. Seeds of the plants that were new to him, and there were very many, he attempted to send back to his brother at the York nursery or to Kew Gardens. Some tree ferns were sent as plants, as was the eucalyptus tree. Unfortunately, Thomas Backhouse did not keep a separate list of the flora sent to him, but the Director of Kew Gardens was very appreciative of his donations and carefully acknowledged them.

James Backhouse returned home to find that Thomas Backhouse, although by no means trained in horticulture, had nevertheless built up a respected and thriving business in York, whilst his unmarried sister looked after the two children. James, in getting to know his children again, passed on his love of plants to his son James, and together they went on botanical expeditions to the more remote parts of Britain, and to Norway and into the Arctic circle, where they discovered a growing passion for alpine plants, for which the Backhouse nursery became justly famous.

George Hudson, the notorious 'Railway King', bought the nursery site in 1839 for the North-Eastern Line railway station and offices and the Backhouse firm moved first to Fishergate and later to a green field site in

Holgate, Acomb. The young James Backhouse married and in 1853 built a house named West Bank on a site adjoining the Holgate nursery. His father died in 1869, but not before he and his son had laid the foundations for one of the first rock gardens in England, anticipating the one in Kew by twenty years.

The nursery became even more famous under the young James, becoming known as The Northern Kew Gardens. It was actually larger than Kew, eventually covering 100 acres (Kew was seventy-five acres at that time). The rock garden in particular drew visitors from many countries – there was also an imitation mountain tarn, as well as streams, crags, scree for the alpine plants and an underground cavern, with artificial lighting for ferns, all flourishing because of the attention paid to the individual needs of the plant.

Gardeners trained at the nursery were in great demand, and the teaching at the Holgate garden became a pattern for later horticultural colleges. Rock and alpine plants, bulbs and ferns were continually bred, raised and propagated, as a browse through the catalogues will testify. The extensive catalogues of new hybrids of daffodils and narcissi bred over the years by the Backhouse nursery are of particular interest.

Lord and Lady Hamilton bought West Bank, along with the nursery, in about 1910. Their son Alex trained as a nurseryman and became manager but he died aged forty and the nursery declined. After the death of Lady Hamilton, the house became an Elizabeth Fry Home, providing training for mothers who had come before the courts for child neglect. York City Council bought much of the land upon which the nursery stood and it became West Bank Park in 1938.

We all love the daffodils which, every spring, dance on the walls of York. There is a story which suggests that they were originally planted because, seeing a pile of unsold bulbs, the manager proposed that rather than throwing them away, he would put them to a lasting and colourful use and thus he planted them on the city walls. I hope the story is true, for daffodils and the Backhouse family name are associated right up to the 1950s. The daffodils which each spring throng those ancient walls of York are a fitting memorial to the York nurseries and to the plantsmen of the Backhouse family.

FROM ALL WALKS OF LIFE

The early herbalists started it all; the wise women who gathered the herbs needed for their potions, from those concocted for the lovelorn to serious remedies for the ailments of the day, a linctus for a bad chest, a salve to clear an infection, a poultice for a boil or an abscess. The monks, too, shared this knowledge of plants and they organised infirmaries, passing on their skills to the early apothecaries and the doctors.

And then came the plant enthusiasts whose interests embraced all plant life, appreciating the endless kaleidoscope of colour and scent from all over the world.

Many, if not most, of these early enthusiasts would these days be termed as amateurs, self-taught, as their passion for plants drove them to delve more deeply, to increase their knowledge and then to pass it on to others. As they came from many walks of life, their diversity of specific interests widened.

Thus we find kings and queens, lords and ladies, politicians, soap boilers, ostlers, drapers, farmers, clergymen all enjoying friendships and increasing their botanical, horticultural and geographic knowledge because of this shared ferment and enthusiasm. Inevitably some concentrated on the nurturing of new seeds and plants, some established centres of learning such as Chelsea or Kew and botanical gardens in many parts of the world, and chairs were set up at universities. The ramifications are as diverse as their backgrounds.

Two very different Quakers who pursued their own particular interests were Thomas Goldney and William Woodville. THOMAS GOLDNEY (1696–1768), a Bristol Quaker, is probably better known as an early garden designer, interested not only in the plants and the conditions under which they would flourish, but also in the settings for the plants: he incorporated a grotto for ferns, walled gardens for shelter and for climbing plants, a canal for the aquatics, and terraces for plants enjoying particular aspects. He built a tower where, no doubt, he and his friends could enjoy an overall view of the garden.

In about 1732, he inherited the family home Goldney Hall, where the gardens were already laid out with walks, summerhouses and an orangery with regularly fruiting citrus trees. Four years later, Thomas Goldney started his Garden Book, meticulously recording the plans and progress of the buildings and gardens, his plantings, the successes and failures. In 1737 he began the work on the subterranean tunnel and the famous grotto. In addition a tower was designed to house a pump and steam engine (from the Ironbridge Quakers) which enabled a waterfall in the grotto, a fountain in the canal and a viewing platform from which to take an overall view of the gardens and surrounding countryside.

After Thomas Goldney's death in 1768 the garden suffered many changes, many of them detrimental, but in the 1930s the house and estate were bought by a discerning couple named Eberle, who were interested in the history of the Quaker family as well as in the unusual garden. They restored the house and the orangery, drained and relined the canal and planted gardens and terraces according to the plans in Thomas Goldney's Garden Book. The property was sold in 1956 at the request of Mrs Eberle to the University of Bristol; the house became accommodation for about thirty students and the orangery became the refectory. In 1969 the paddock, bought over 200 years earlier by Thomas Goldney for £300, became the site for new residential accommodation for 200 students. Many of the features of the garden still remain and are in the care of the university.

In recent years much work has been done to restore them in the spirit of his original design. The grotto, a Grade 1 listed building, is widely valued for its unusual atmosphere and construction; it now receives about 10,000 visitors a year and is often the subject of articles and papers. The Hall itself is frequently used as a film location, such as for *Truly, Madly, Deeply*, as well as for the BBC's *Chronicles of Narnia*, and *Only Fools and Horses Christmas Special 2002*.

A man with a very different botanical interest was WILLIAM WOODVILLE (1752–1805). He was born at Cockermouth in Cumberland and was one of the medical Quakers of the eighteenth century whose professional and outside interests coalesced. He received a good education and, after an apprenticeship with an apothecary, took a medical degree at Edinburgh University. After travelling on the continent, visiting medical centres of learning, he returned to Britain, first to Scotland and then to London where, in 1791, he was appointed physician at the Smallpox and Inoculation Hospital in St Pancras.

His botanical interests, allied with medicine, resulted in the publication of a major work in three volumes. *Medical Botany, containing Systematic and General Descriptions, with plates, of all the Medicinal Plants, indigenous and exotic, comprehended in the Catalogues of the Materia Medica, as published by the Royal Colleges of Physicians of London and Edinburgh: accompanied with a circumstantial Detail of their Medicinal Effects, and of the diseases in which they have been most successfully employed.* This is considered a classic of its type.

William Woodville carried out extensive vaccination trials at the Smallpox Hospital on a large number of patients, and in 1796 he published *The History of the inoculation of Smallpox in Great Britain; comprehending a* *review of all the publications on the subject; with an experimental enquiry into the relative advantages of every measure which has been deemed necessary in the process of inoculation.* This was to have been in two volumes, but he cancelled the second volume following Dr Jenner's discovery of a new method of vaccination. William Woodville at first opposed this but later, admitting his mistake, became a staunch supporter. A sincere Quaker, he was buried at Bunhill Fields Quaker burial ground in London.

'THE UNIVERSE IS ALWAYS SINGING'

After the middle of the nineteenth century the emphasis moved to more detailed studies, for example the morphology of a particular species or the breeding and hybridisation of plants, and we find many Quakers holding chairs in botany both in this country and abroad. Some were very influential in helping to expand the established centres of botanical interest, such as Kew Gardens, or the Chelsea Physic Garden, and the botanical gardens of Scotland and Wales. Some of the botanists went abroad to study, record and classify the flora of the less developed parts of the world. The nurserymen continued, often specialising in a few species, to breed new cultivars for a growing market.

Retired Shanghai silk merchant THOMAS HANBURY (1832–1907), whose grandfather, father and elder brother were part of the pharmaceutical firm of Allen and Hanbury, bought an estate in Liguria, Northern Italy, called 'La Mortola', a neglected garden surrounding the derelict Palazzio Marenga discovered by his brother Daniel. It has been suggested that Thomas Hanbury intended it to be a sort of halfway house for plants from the tropical forests, those that needed a different climate and often more growing space than could be provided by the greenhouses and stove houses in England.

Skilful botanists were called from Germany, exchanges were organised of gardeners and scholars abroad, especially with Kew Gardens, and special zones were created to group plants gathered together for their phytogeographic or ecological or aesthetic peculiarities. This criterion inspired the creation of the Japanese Garden, the Australian Forest, the collection of roses, that of succulent plants, the Garden of Perfumes and many other special areas.

The garden at 'La Mortola' in Italy was badly neglected after Hanbury's death. It was given to the University of Genoa in 1960 in the hope that it would become a leading botanical garden once again; dedicated men and women in both Italy and Britain have worked hard to re-establish it. Among the numerous Italian and foreign gardens which may be visited today, the Hanbury Botanic Gardens occupy quite a special place. They represent, in fact, an exceptional acclimatisation area where exotic plants from all over the world grow together in the open air, though out of their natural environment. It is this wonderful 'cohabitation' that makes the charm of the Hanbury Botanical Gardens: as seasons change, the Gardens display a range of colours and forms such as only Nature can offer.

While in Italy, Thomas Hanbury also set up schools, a library, and founded and maintained a Department of Botany in the University of Genoa in 1892.

His greatest legacy, however, centres on a house and garden he bought in England at Wisley near Woking in Surrey. This had been the property of a plantsman whose main passion was for growing water lilies. Thomas Hanbury maintained the sixty acres, having money to spend on gardeners and new gardening methods, and in 1903 presented the estate to the Royal Horticultural Society. Wisley, now of worldwide renown, has been greatly enlarged since that time and continues to expand in size and in reputation.

Several Quakers were associated with the Royal Botanic Garden at Kew, all academics and hard-working botanists, and five were associated with Brentford and Isleworth Quaker Meeting (Daniel Oliver, John Gilbert Baker, Richard Eric Holttum, Jan Bevington Gillet, and William Thomas Stearn). They gave service to the Religious Society of Friends (Quakers) for almost 150 years – a remarkable record for one Quaker meeting.

DANIEL OLIVER (1830–1916), born in Newcastle upon Tyne, was appointed to the staff of the Herbarium at Kew, as Keeper and Librarian, for 36 years from 1858. He was also Professor of Botany at the University College London, starting his lectures early to enable him to spend the rest of the day at Kew. For fifteen years he gave voluntary lectures to gardeners at Kew.

Daniel Oliver's lectures were later made

57

official and continued by the second of the Quaker botanists at Brentford and Isleworth Meeting, JOHN GILBERT BAKER (1834–99). He too was a northerner, born at Guisborough, and he succeeded Daniel Oliver as Keeper of the Herbarium at Kew. His son, EDMUND BAKER (1864–1949) was appointed to the botanical section of the Natural History Museum in Kensington.

RICHARD ERIC HOLTTUM (1895–1990) had a long and adventurous life. During World War I he served on the Western Front with the Friends' Ambulance Unit, an organisation formed by Quakers which consisted of people from all walks of life who were conscientious objectors.

After resuming his studies at Cambridge University Eric Holttum graduated in 1920 with a first class honours degree in Botany, and for 32 years worked for the promotion of tropical botany and horticulture. He accompanied Professor A. C. Seward to Greenland to collect fossils of former tropical plants of that area, and in 1922 was appointed Assistant Director of the Singapore Botanic Garden, where he became Director of Research in 1925, extending his fieldwork to Borneo and Java. From this work developed the important orchid growing industry in Malaya, alongside bamboo, ginger and ferns. In 1942, the Japanese army took control of Singapore, but he was asked to stay in charge of the gardens until a Japanese professor of botany could replace him. When the Japanese professor arrived, Holttum asked to be interned with his compatriots, a request that was denied. He was ordered to carry on with his research work into orchids and ferns. After the war he resumed his position as Director of the Botanic Gardens until, in 1949, he was appointed Professor of Botany in the new University of Malaya in Singapore. During his long retirement he worked voluntarily at the Herbarium in Kew and continued his studies in tropical botany.

JAN BEVINGTON GILLETT (born 1911) was educated at the Leighton Park Quaker School in Reading, and in 1930 went to work at the Kew Herbarium. He was sent to Rhodesia as a member of a botanical expedition, later working in Ethiopia and Iraq. From 1949 he was involved in the preparation of a catalogue of the flora of tropical East Africa. After twenty years he retired to live in Kew, working voluntarily in the Herbarium, and mainly studying the plant families *Leguminosae* and *Burseraceae*.

Professor WILLIAM THOMAS STEARN (1911–2001), joined the staff of the botany department at the Natural History Museum in

South Kensington, retiring as Principal Scientific Officer in the department of botany after spending almost twenty years as librarian to the Royal Horticultural Society. He wrote his first scientific paper at the age of eighteen and went on to contribute 470 publications on botany, horticulture and bibliography. At the beginning of World War II, he went to live in Kew, and was accepted into membership at Brentford and Isleworth Quaker meeting.

Stearn spent some time studying the flora of Jamaica and Greece and his interests lay also in the field of early botanical literature. His knowledge and works led to acclaim and recognition from Universities in Leiden and in Sweden. He was President of the Linnaean Society for three years and then worked on a new work on the achievements of Linnaeus. He was described as one of the great botanists of the twentieth century.

DOROTHY ADLINGTON CADBURY (1892–1987), was a hard-working director of Cadbury Bros, the chocolate firm in Birmingham. In her spare time, however, her interests lay far from the field of business; her lifelong hobby was botany and her love of wild flowers. She joined the Wild Flower Society in 1937, painstakingly sending in her new records every March.

The beginning of the war found her on the Isle of Mull, taking part in a botanical survey. Later in the permanent collection of the British Museum of Natural History we find her studies of pondweeds (*Potamogeton*).

As her interest grew and deepened she spent the first ten years of her retirement working with Professor Hawkes at Birmingham University to produce, in 1971, *A computer-mapped Flora. A study of the County of Warwickshire*, D. A. Cadbury, J. G. Hawkes, R. C. Readett. This study broke new ground, exciting the interest of many field botanists, and was, we believe, the first time that computer mapping had been used to enhance the recording of plant species.

The county was divided into one kilometre squares and meticulous recordings of plant species were superimposed. Mary Penny, the daughter of a cousin of Dorothy Cadbury, was one of the many people drawn into the project, together with several field naturalists, amateur and professional. Mary recalls the enthusiasm and delight she enjoyed, sallying forth with her mother and Dorothy, armed with books, mapping and recording instruments, helping her cousin to 'do her squares'.

One of the last great plant hunters, EDWARD KENT BALLS (1892–1984), spent World War I as a Quaker Relief Worker in Serbia and Russia. His early knowledge and expertise in

opposite
Oenothera rosea
(a Bartram/Collinson
introduction)
Audrey Jennett

the fields of botany and horticulture was gathered through apprenticeships in nurseries, but in 1932 he accompanied the Treasurer of the Alpine Society to Persia, bringing back the first Dionysia, after which he made the decision to become a professional plant hunter, and later, a writer and lecturer. He faced similar dangers and hardships to the early plant hunters, on one occasion being arrested on suspicion of being Lawrence of Arabia! Edward Balls lived many years in California and in Spain, dying in Yorkshire aged ninety-two.

There are many Quaker nurserymen today, continuing and extending the work of these eighteenth and nineteenth century Quaker gardeners. ALAN BLOOM founded a nursery at Bressingham in Norfolk after the Second World War, which was for many years the foremost wholesale supplier of plants in the country specialising in herbaceous perennials. He devised a public show garden with a series of island beds which display more than 5,000 species. Alan Bloom, together with his son Adrian and the chief propagator, Percy Piper, have introduced many new cultivars. They include *Crocosmia* 'Lucifer', *Kniphofia* 'Percy's Pride', *Kniphofia* 'Bressingham Comet', *Phlox paniculata* 'Harlequin', *Aconitum* 'Bressingham Spire' and many others.

The 47 island beds, designed and introduced by Alan (who sadly died just as this publication was nearing completion), show off his wide and varied collection of plants including many Bressingham raised varieties. Alan was one of the most respected plantsman of the twentieth century, and he could often be found talking with visitors outside his home,

Bressingham Hall. Jaime Blake, his son-in-law, carries on the family tradition as curator of this historic garden, maintaining and developing it and the collection of plants. The garden centre, the nurseries and the Bressingham Steam Museum provide a happy and educational day out for thousands of people each year, many of whom would have been driven around in a miniature train by Alan Bloom, a keen steam enthusiast. Alan was one of the founders of the Hardy Plants Society and was its President at the time of his death. The Bloom family combine a deep knowledge and love of plants with business acumen, which has resulted in the opening of their nurseries and gardens for the education and enjoyment of those of us who love plants, enjoy gardens, but would never presume to be called experts or botanists.

On the 'Quaker Botanists' panel of the Quaker Tapestry is a quotation from a young Quaker botanist, SARAH MARTHA BAKER, who was born in 1887. After studying at University College London, where she became a valued lecturer particularly on plant biochemistry, she was invited to become a Fellow of the Royal Society early in her career, but died before she could accept this honour. Her death, when she was only 29, came as a blow to her scientific and Quaker friends alike.

Sarah Baker taught in the Sunday school at Willesden Quaker Meeting for many years and the pupils there recall her teaching that 'the Universe is always singing, while only man is silent; and that man must learn to listen, so that his heart may join the universal chorus', the words to be found on the Quaker Botanists' panel of the Quaker Tapestry.

BOTANICAL ARTISTS

You will no doubt be enjoying the botanical illustrations in this book. Such drawings have played an important and essential part in the story of plantsmen and women; we already know of Ann Lee and Sydney Parkinson, of William Curtis and the rise of *The Botanical Magazine*.

There are many Quaker artists who enjoy the special challenge of botanical illustration. Sara Anne (Sally) Schofield is a founder member of the Society of Botanical Artists and has pictures in private collections worldwide. As a child her one aim was to paint flowers and her artistic aspirations were encouraged by her parents, themselves both well-known artists. She studied at Twickenham College of Art and while there began freelance drawing for a West Africa Flora followed by work in the herbarium of the Royal Botanic Gardens, Kew, enjoying the detailed accuracy required by the botanists.

Sara has had many exhibitions, three of them in London, and has shown with major art societies and at many galleries in the UK, frequently with subjects other than flowers. In the USA her work is represented in The Hunt Institute of Botanical Documentation in Pittsburgh, and The Shirley Sherwood Collection of Contemporary Botanical Artists. She holds two RHS gold medals for her botanical paintings.

Sally became a member of the Society of Friends at the age of eleven when she attended Staines Meeting, but most of her Quaker friendships were with young people at the larger Brentworth and Isleworth Meeting and it was there that she came into contact with Quaker botanists and with Kew. She is now a member of Purley Meeting.

Two women who have given their time and talents to the production of the illustrations in this book for the benefit of the Quaker Tapestry Scheme are Audrey Jennett and Anne Dent, both early members of the Northern Society for Botanical Art, enjoying the many classes and courses provided and taking certificates and diplomas. Now a member of York Monthly Meeting, Audrey Jennett is a versatile artist, enjoying drawing and painting, but after her retirement she became especially involved in botanical illustration. She was one of the embroidery group who, when living in Sheffield, worked on the Coalbrookdale panel of the Quaker Tapestry, helping with the drawings, the choice of colours and being responsible for the embroidery of the vivid flames and, as she says, 'the kiln on the right-

hand side'. Her interest in the Tapestry over many years led to her involvement with this book, and with her came her friend and fellow artist, Anne Dent.

Anne Dent is a member of Sheffield Central Meeting; she is a retired teacher of botany and biology, who concentrated her artistic skills on botanical illustration. She regularly exhibits at the RHS exhibition of Botanical Artists, being a silver medalist. The plants that thrive near the limestone country of Derbyshire provide one of the themed topics which she enjoys researching and illustrating; other researches, on parasitic and semi-parasitic plants and on saltmarsh seaweeds have provided very different subjects.

The drawings made by Audrey Jennett and Anne Dent make a valuable and unique contribution to this book, and continue the aims of the Quaker Tapestry – to use and celebrate the many different talents brought to the scheme.

Ann Nichols (*left*), the author of this book, and Anne Dent (*right*), one of the botanical artists whose work is shown

The entrance to the
front garden of the
Quaker meeting house
at Kendal

Chelone obliqua,
a detail from the
cartoon for
'Quaker Botanists',
panel D8 of the
Quaker Tapestry

right
Rose 'Quaker Star'

THE QUAKER GARDEN AT KENDAL

The one-way traffic system in the Lakeland
town of Kendal sweeps from Stramongate and
runs along the river Kent before crossing
Miller Bridge. The car traveller may well miss
the oasis of calm, the front garden of the
Quaker meeting house, but the pedestrian
visitor can push open the handsome iron gates
and stroll through the walled garden to the
doors of the meeting house and to the Quaker
Tapestry Exhibition.

The garden was once a Quaker burial
ground and the simple headstones have been
re-laid alongside the path. A sundial sits
among the stones, surrounded by the pebbles
which were contributed by Quakers from
around the world, as a celebration of the life of
Anne Wynn-Wilson – the inspiration behind
the Quaker Tapestry.

Beyond the sundial is a lush green lawn,
upon which are two wooden benches inviting
visitors to rest awhile. A wide herbaceous
border lies beneath the stately windows of the
exhibition centre, containing many plants
introduced to this country in the eighteenth
and nineteenth centuries by Quaker
plantsmen. These include *Chelone obliqua*
(left), a pink flowered perennial introduced by
John Bartram, which features on the tapestry.
Bartram also introduced several members of
the phlox family to these shores, hybrids of
which are well represented in this border, and
the mountain variety, *Phlox subulata*, which
can be found among the gravestones.

The garden is not exclusively made up of
Quaker-introduced species, however. For
example, if you visit the garden in spring a
magnificent *Magnolia soulangiana* will be in
full bloom. This magnolia has long flourished
at the side of the main door, but it is not one of
the varieties introduced by Friends such as
Magnolia acuminata, a mountain magnolia

introduced from the South Eastern USA in 1743, which grows one hundred feet high in its native setting.

On the opposite side of the path, against the wall, there is a thick border of the deepest blue gentians, *Gentiana acaulis*, which were planted by a dear friend of the meeting and are going from strength to strength. Behind these is a bed of 'Quaker Star' roses (opposite), which fill the summer months with an abundance of glorious red blooms. These beautiful flowers share their name with the eight-pointed Quaker Star which has served as the Friends' insignia since 1870, and serve to remind us of the Nobel peace prize awarded in 1947 for the joint efforts of British and American Quakers to relieve suffering during two World Wars.

A wrought iron seat rests next to the Quaker Stars. Beyond this can be found the rose 'Abraham Darby', which was named after the Quaker iron founding family from Coalbrookdale, Shropshire. The Darby family were the builders of the world's first iron bridge, around which has grown the town of Ironbridge on the river Severn. Beside these is the third rose in the garden, 'Peace', bred by Robert Pyle, an American Quaker.

Turning to face the lawn, you may well wonder at the small protective fence circling a group of white flowers growing amongst the grass. These are meadow saxifrage, *Saxifraga granulata* (below) and are included in 'The list of rarer plants' in the annals of Kendal, 1832. A single stem was discovered in the grass in April 1994, and having been carefully tended is now an expanding patch of white flowers. It may well have been one of the native plants seen by Thomas Lawson, known as the 'father of Lakeland botany', and it is a delight to all that this rare native plant has chosen to reappear in the lawn of the meeting house.

To the left of the lawn, underneath the spreading boughs of a tree, is the 'wild garden', an area of wild flowers (many of which are native) with a log pile to the rear. This area

The garden

encourages insects and birds into the garden, increasing its biodiversity. It is at its most beautiful on an early Spring morning, when the dew glistens on the grass. This bed is still under development, and changing all the time. Two compost bins have also been installed in this area, in which waste from the tearoom kitchen is recycled and later used on the garden.

The garden has grown over the years under the care of Ann Cuming, who moved here from Birmingham in the early years of the exhibition. Her unstinting efforts won her an award in the 'Kendal Pride' campaign in 1999. She now has more time to enjoy the pleasures of her labours, as the garden has moved into the care of Karen Tansley, a local gardener who is working to develop the garden over the coming seasons. Karen can often be found pushing her trusty mower up and down the lawn, ever striving toward perfect 'bowling green' stripes. She is always happy to take five minutes to chat to visitors about the garden.

The garden will continue to change over the seasons and years to come. New plants will be introduced, old ones may be lost, but the essence will remain the same, and as well as being a quiet spot to while away a sunny hour it will also continue to be a living, growing reminder of the Quaker plantsmen of the eighteenth and nineteenth centuries, who made it possible.

left
Saxifraga granulata

bq - british quaker
aq - american quaker
nq - non quaker

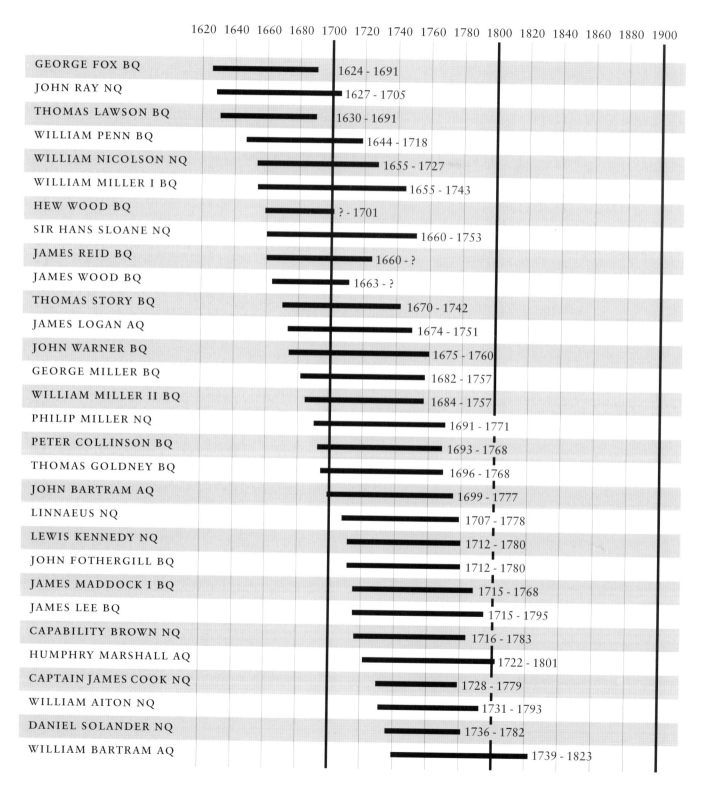

Time lines

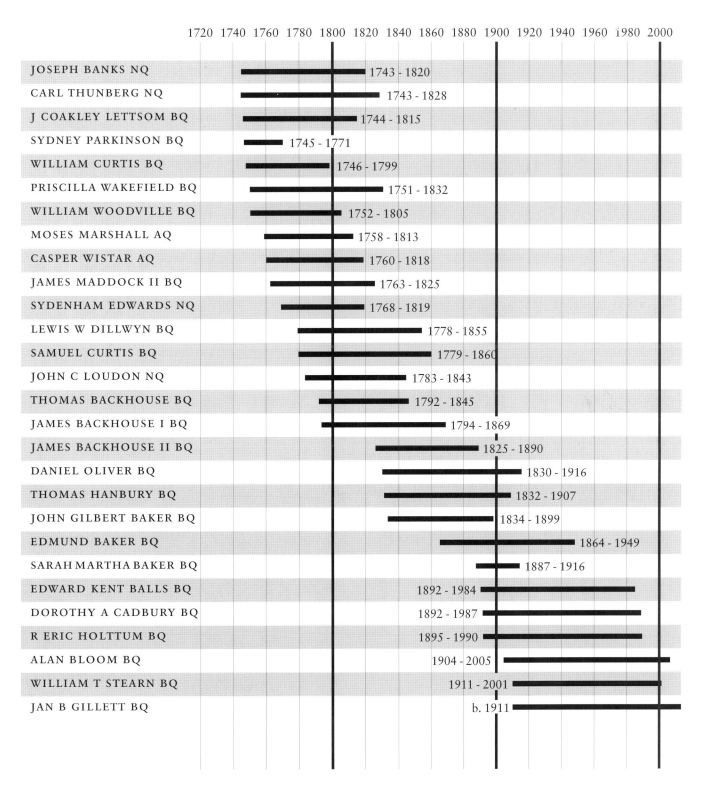

	1720	1740	1760	1780	1800	1820	1840	1860	1880	1900	1920	1940	1960	1980	2000

JOSEPH BANKS NQ — 1743 - 1820

CARL THUNBERG NQ — 1743 - 1828

J COAKLEY LETTSOM BQ — 1744 - 1815

SYDNEY PARKINSON BQ — 1745 - 1771

WILLIAM CURTIS BQ — 1746 - 1799

PRISCILLA WAKEFIELD BQ — 1751 - 1832

WILLIAM WOODVILLE BQ — 1752 - 1805

MOSES MARSHALL AQ — 1758 - 1813

CASPER WISTAR AQ — 1760 - 1818

JAMES MADDOCK II BQ — 1763 - 1825

SYDENHAM EDWARDS NQ — 1768 - 1819

LEWIS W DILLWYN BQ — 1778 - 1855

SAMUEL CURTIS BQ — 1779 - 1860

JOHN C LOUDON NQ — 1783 - 1843

THOMAS BACKHOUSE BQ — 1792 - 1845

JAMES BACKHOUSE I BQ — 1794 - 1869

JAMES BACKHOUSE II BQ — 1825 - 1890

DANIEL OLIVER BQ — 1830 - 1916

THOMAS HANBURY BQ — 1832 - 1907

JOHN GILBERT BAKER BQ — 1834 - 1899

EDMUND BAKER BQ — 1864 - 1949

SARAH MARTHA BAKER BQ — 1887 - 1916

EDWARD KENT BALLS BQ — 1892 - 1984

DOROTHY A CADBURY BQ — 1892 - 1987

R ERIC HOLTTUM BQ — 1895 - 1990

ALAN BLOOM BQ — 1904 - 2005

WILLIAM T STEARN BQ — 1911 - 2001

JAN B GILLETT BQ — b. 1911

Glossary of people mentioned in the text

AITON, WILLIAM (1731–93): Gardener in the Chelsea Physic Garden. In 1759 became the director of Kew Gardens. Author of *Hortus Kewensis*.

BACKHOUSE, JAMES, THE ELDER (1794–1869): British Quaker, nurseryman in York in partnership with his brother Thomas. He travelled in the ministry with Friend George Washington Walker to Australia and Tasmania.

BACKHOUSE, JAMES, THE YOUNGER (1825–90): British Quaker, plant collector (Britain and Norway). Son of James Backhouse (1794–1869).

BACKHOUSE, THOMAS (1792–1845): British Quaker. With his brother, James, bought Telford's nursery in York.

BANKS, JOSEPH (1743–1820): From an early age, Joseph Banks was passionate about natural history, and in particular, botany. In 1766 he travelled to Newfoundland and Labrador to collect plants, animals and rocks and in the same year was elected a Fellow of the Royal Society. When in 1768 the Royal Society initiated Captain Cook's expedition to Tahiti, Banks obtained permission from the Admiralty to take a party of his own in order to collect and study new plants in unknown lands. He was knighted in 1781.

BARTRAM, JOHN (1699–1777): American Quaker, self-taught botanist. Called by Linnaeus 'the greatest natural botanist in the world'.

BARTRAM, WILLIAM (1739–1823): American Quaker, traveller, botanist and botanical artist. Author of *Travels through North and South Carolina, etc.* (1791).

BROWN, LANCELOT (CAPABILITY) (1716–83): English gardener designer who developed gardens at Blenheim, Warwick Castle, Kew Gardens and many other locations.

COLLINSON, PETER (1693–1768): British Quaker, woollen draper, botanist and naturalist. Through his business and Quaker connections and trade with the Americas he introduced British plants to America and vice versa. FRS(1728).

COOK, CAPTAIN JAMES (1728–79): English navigator. In 1768 he took the ship *Endeavour* to the Pacific in order to observe the Transit of Venus.

CURTIS, SAMUEL (1779–1860): British Quaker, nurseryman, who became publisher of *The Botanical Magazine* after the death of his cousin William Curtis.

CURTIS, WILLIAM (1746–99): British Quaker, writer, lecturer, and founder in 1787 of *The Botanical Magazine*. In 1771 he set up a botanical garden of British plants at Bermondsey, and in 1773 he was appointed demonstrator of plants at the Chelsea Physic Garden.

DARBY, ABRAHAM (1750–91): British Quaker. The Darby family were the builders of the world's first iron bridge at Ironbridge. Abraham Darby's grandfather (also Abraham Darby) was an iron manufacturer who developed, in 1709, a process for smelting iron ore using coke rather than charcoal.

DILLWYN, LEWIS WESTON (1778–1855): British Quaker. His library of around 1,000 volumes illustrating the development of botany from the sixteenth to the nineteenth century is housed in the National Library of Wales.

EDWARDS, SYDENHAM (1768–1819): Welshman. The most prolific and talented botanical artist of his time, illustrating for *The Botanical Magazine* and then in 1815 he started his own magazine *The Botanical Register*.

FELL, MARGARET (1614–1702): known as 'the mother of Quakerism'. She was married to Judge Thomas Fell and lived at Swarthmoor Hall in Ulverston, Cumbria. In 1652 she became convinced of the truth of George Fox's ministry. She married George Fox in 1669, eleven years after the death of Judge Fell.

FOTHERGILL, JOHN, MD (1712–80): British Quaker, physician, philanthropist, botanist and plant collector. FRS (1763).

FOX, GEORGE (1624–91): founder of the Society of Friends (Quakers).

GERARD, JOHN (1545–1612): English herbalist – his garden was famous for rare plants. Author of *Herball or Generall Historie of Plantes* (1597).

GOLDNEY, THOMAS (1696–1768): Bristol Quaker, with business interests in banking, shipping and the iron industry, and a keen gardener and garden designer. Goldney Hall is now part of Bristol University, and the gardens are occasionally open to the public.

HANBURY, THOMAS (1832–1907): A Quaker philanthropist and great lover of plants who donated Wisley to the Royal Horticultural Society and in 1867 established The Giardini Botanici Hanbury, known as La Mortola.

HATSHEPSUT, QUEEN OF EGYPT: (reigned 1490–1469 BC) daughter of Thutmose I and Queen Ahmose who married her stepbrother (Thutmose II) after the death of the King. When Thutmose II died Thutmose III became Pharaoh. As he was a minor, Hatshepsut became his regent. She appointed herself Pharaoh and dispatched an expedition to Punt (now Somalia) on the African coast – the myrrh trees were brought back to Egypt to adorn the temple of Deir el-Bahri.

LAWSON, THOMAS (1630–91): became a Quaker in 1652, a member of the Valiant Sixty.

LEE, JAMES (1715–95) British Quaker, nurseryman, joint proprietor with Lewis Kennedy of the Vineyard Nursery, Hammersmith.

LETTSOM, JOHN COAKLEY (1744–1815): British Quaker, physician, prison reformer, philanthropist, and prolific letter writer. FRS (1773).

LINNAEUS (CARL VON LINNÉ) (1707–78): Swedish naturalist and founder of modern nomenclature for plants and animals. FRS (1753).

LOGAN, JAMES (1674–1751): American Quaker, colonial statesman and scholar. Born in Ireland. He emigrated to Philadelphia with Penn and remained his confidential adviser for many years.

LOUDON, JOHN CLAUDIUS (1783–1843): Horticultural writer, designer. He compiled an *Encyclopaedia of Gardening* (1822), founded and edited the *Architectural Magazine* (1834) and was the author of *Arboretum Brittanicum* (8 vols, 1838) which was solely on the subject of trees and shrubs.

MADDOCK, JAMES, THE ELDER (1715–86): British Quaker, founder of the Walworth Nurseries, and author of *The Florist's Directory, a treatise on the culture of flowers*, published posthumously by his son in 1786.

MADDOCK, JAMES, THE YOUNGER (1764–?): British Quaker nurseryman who ran the Walworth Nurseries with his father.

MARSHALL, HUMPHRY (1722–1801): American Quaker, plant hunter, cousin of the botanist John Bartram, and through Bartram built up a correspondence with a number of British botanists including John Fothergill, Peter Collinson, Joseph Banks and John Coakley Lettsom.

MARSHALL, MOSES (1758–1813): American Quaker, he studied medicine, but gave up his practice to assist his uncle (Humphry Marshall) in his expanding botanical and horticultural enterprise. He became a skilled botanist in his own right, but gave up botanizing in later life in order to fulfil his commitments as Justice of the Peace in Chester County.

MILLER, PHILIP (1691–1771): set up in business as a florist at St George's Fields; Gardener of Chelsea Physic Garden (1722-1770); corresponded with Carl Linnaeus and many other foreign botanists; left a large herbarium which was purchased by Sir Joseph Banks and is now in the Natural History Museum. FRS (1730).

MILLER, WILLIAM (1655–1743): British Quaker, nurseryman and gardener. He became gardener at the Abbey of Holyrood House. His eldest son, George Miller, followed his father as head gardener at Holyrood House, and later became gardener to the Duke of Hamilton. William Miller, his second son, went into business as a seedsman and nurseryman, and his grandson, also William Miller, succeeded to the post of head gardener of Holyrood House and took over the flourishing seed and nursery business.

NICOLSON, WILLIAM (1655–1727): Bishop of Carlisle, historian and antiquarian. Author of *Seventeenth Century Flora of Cumbria*. Friend of Thomas Lawson. FRS (1705).

PARKINSON, JOHN (1567–1650): London herbalist. Author of *Paradisi in sole: Paradisus terrestris, or A garden of all sorts of pleasant flowers which our English Ayre will permit to be noursed up*.

PARKINSON, SYDNEY (1745–71): British Quaker and illustrator. He travelled with Captain Cook on the ship *Endeavour* to the Pacific in order to illustrate plants for Joseph Banks.

PENN, WILLIAM (1644–1718): British Quaker, sent down from Oxford for refusing to conform to the Anglican Church. He attended Quaker meetings in Ireland, where he was convinced. Imprisoned for his beliefs in Ireland, the Tower of London, and Newgate Prison and eventually travelled to America and became the founder of Pennsylvania (1680). FRS (1681).

RAY, JOHN (1627–1705): Seventeenth-century English Clergyman, naturalist and botanist and author of *Catalogus Plantarum Angliae*. FRS (1667).

REID, JAMES (or REED – born *c.* 1660): Irish Quaker, plant collector for the King's garden at Hampton Court.

SLOANE, SIR HANS (1660–1753): British physician and naturalist. Supporter of the Chelsea Physic Garden, and bequeathed his substantial library to the British Museum (around 200,000 specimens). FRS (1685).

SOLANDER, DANIEL (1733–82) Swedish botanist who studied at Uppsala University under Carl von Linné or Linnaeus. He travelled with Captain Cook, Joseph Banks and Sydney Parkinson on the *Endeavour*. FRS (1764).

STORY, THOMAS (c.1670–1742): British Quaker, and friend of William Penn. In 1698 he travelled to America where he met with many Quaker communities before returning, in 1715, to his family home near Carlisle.

THUNBERG, CARL PETER (1743–1828): Swedish naturalist. He was a pupil of Linnaeus at Uppsala University. There he studied natural philosophy and medicine. FRS (1788).

TRADESCANT, JOHN, THE ELDER (*c.*1570–1638), gardener (he was head gardener to King Charles I) and plant hunter. He founded the first public museum (now the Ashmolean Museum in Oxford).

TRADESCANT, JOHN, THE YOUNGER (1608–62): gardener and plant hunter. He succeeded his father as head gardener to King Charles I.

WAKEFIELD, PRISCILLA (1751–1832): British Quaker, author of many books for children and of *An Introduction to Botany, in a Series of Familiar Letters, with Illustrative Engravings*. Known as 'Wakefield's Botany' it went into 11 editions over 40 years.

WALKER, GEORGE WASHINGTON (1800–59): British Quaker who, with James Backhouse, travelled through the Australian and African colonies between 1832 and 1841.

WARNER, JOHN (1674/5–1760): British Quaker Jacob Hagan gave a cutting of the 'Black Hamburgh' vine to John Warner, who in turn gave cuttings to friends, including Charles Raymond. He in turn gave it to 'Capability' Brown who planted it at Hampton Court.

WISTAR, CASPAR (1760–1818): American Quaker of German descent, physician. The plant genus Wisteria was named in his honour.

WOOD, HEW (died 1701): Scottish Quaker, nurseryman and gardener to the Duke of Hamilton.

WOOD, JAMES (born 1663): Scottish Quaker, gardener to the Duke of Queensbury.

WOODVILLE, WILLIAM (1752–1805): British Quaker, physician, and botanist. Author of *Medical Botany*. He was made a Fellow of the Linnaean Society in honour of his botanical work, in particular the establishment of a garden at King's Cross.

WYNNE-WILSON, ANNE (1926–1998): British Quaker, founder of the Quaker Tapestry. The following is an extract from *Quakers in Stitches*, written by Anne. 'On the first Sunday in January 1981 I began teaching a boy in the Quaker meeting in Taunton. My intention was that we should make a long scroll illustrated with stories from Quaker history. Jonathan, then aged 11, knowing that I was an embroiderer, asked, "Can we do it in embroidery?" The Bayeux Tapestry flashed across my mind and I promised to think about it. Jonathan had dropped the pebble into the pool and the rings are still increasing. His seemingly impossible request could become reality if the work was shared by many people. Embroidery was the catalyst which opened opportunities for an unusual experiment in education, communication and community experience.'

Sources and select bibliography

BACKHOUSE, JAMES A., TYLOR, CHARLES: *The Life and Labours of George Washington Walker, of Hobart Town, Tasmania.* London, 1862.

ibid: *A Narrative of a Visit to the Australian Colonies.* Hamilton Adams, London, 1843.

BACKHOUSE, JAMES A.: *A Narrative of a Visit to the Mauritius and South Africa.* Hamilton Adams, London, 1844.

BANKS, M.R., SMITH, S.J., ORCHARD, A.E., and KANTVILLAS, G. (ed.): *Aspects of Tasmanian botany: a Tribute to Winifred Curtis.* Hobart, Royal Society of Tasmania, 1991.

BARTRAM, WILLIAM: *Travels through North and South Carolina, Georgia, East and West Florida, etc.* James & Johnson, Philadelphia, 1791.

BEAGLEHOLE, JOHN CAWTE (ed.): *The Endeavour Journal of Joseph Banks 1768-1771.* Trustees of the Public Library of New South Wales in association with Angus and Robertson, 1962.

BESSE, JOSEPH: *A Collection of the Sufferings of the People Called Quakers.* Luke Hinde, London, 1753.

BRETT-JAMES, NORMAN G.: *The Life of Peter Collinson,* Dunstan & Co., London, 1925.

CADBURY, D.A., HAWKES, J.G., and READETT, R.C.A.: *Computer-Mapped Flora, A Study of the County of Warwickshire.* Birmingham Natural History Society/Academic Press, London, 1971.

CRUICKSHANK, HELEN GERE (ed.): *John and William Bartram's America: selections from the writings of the Philadelphia Naturalists.* The Devin-Adair Company, New York, 1957.

CURTIS, WILLIAM: *A Catalogue of the British, Medicinal, Culinary, and Agricultural Plants, Cultivated in the London Botanic Gardens, to which are prefixed, proposals for opening it by subscription.* London, 1783.
ibid: Flora Londinensis. 1777-1798.

ibid: *Practical observations on the British grasses, especially such as are best adapted to the laying down or improving of meadows and pastures: likewise an enumeration of the British grasses.* H. D. Symonds, 1812.

ibid: *The Botanical Magazine* (The Kew Magazine incorporating Curtis' Botanical Magazine). 1984.

DARLINGTON, WILLIAM: *Memorials of John Bartram and Humphry Marshall. With notices of their botanical contemporaries.* Lindsay & Blakiston, Philadelphia, 1849.

DILLWYN, LEWIS: *Hortus Collinsonianus. An account of the plants cultivated by the late Peter Collinson.* W. C. Murray & D. Rees, Swansea, 1843.

ELLIS, JOHN: *Directions for bringing over Seeds and Plants from the East Indies and other distant countries in a state of vegetation.* London, 1770.

FIELD, HENRY and SEMPLE, ROBERT HUNTER: *Memoirs of the Botanic Garden at Chelsea.* London, 1878.

FOTHERGILL, JOHN and COLLINSON, PETER: *In a letter to a friend.* London, 1770.

FOTHERGILL, JOHN: *Some Account of the Late Peter Collinson.* London, 1770.

FOX, RICHARD HINGSTON: *Dr John Fothergill and his Friends: Chapters in Eighteenth Century Life.* Macmillan & Co, 1919.

GERARD, JOHN: The *Herball or Generall Historie of Plantes.* London, 1633.

JOSSELYN, JOHN: *New England's Rarities Discovered: in Birds, Beasts, Fishes, Serpents and Plants of that Country.* G. Widdowes, London, 1672.

LAWSON, THOMAS: *Baptismalogia, or a Treatise Concerning Baptisms: Whereto is Added a Discourse Concerning the Supper, Bread and Wine; Called also Communion.* London, 1677-1678.

LETTSOM, DR JOHN COAKLEY: *Hortus Uptoniensis, or a Catalogue of Stove and Greenhouse Plants in Dr Fothergill's Garden at Upton, at the time of his decease.* Privately published, London, 1783(?)

MADDOCK, JAMES: *The Florist's Directory: a Treatise on the Culture of Flowers.* Harding, London, 1822.

MOORE, EMILY E.: *Travelling with Thomas Story. The life and Travels of an Eighteenth-Century Quaker.* Letchworth Printers, Letchworth, 1947.

NICKALLS, JOHN (ed.): *The Journal of George Fox.* Religious Society of Friends, London, 1975.

PARKINSON, JOHN: *Paradisi in sole: Paradisus terrestris.* H. Lownes and R. Young, London, 1629.

PENNEY, NORMAN (ed.): *The Household Account Book of Sarah Fell of Swarthmoor Hall.* University Press, Cambridge, 1920.

PRATT, SAMUEL JACKSON: *Gleanings through Wales, Holland and Westphalia, with views of peace and war at home and abroad. To which is added Humanity . . . revised and corrected.* Sixth edition, 3 vols., London, 1802.

RAISTRICK, ARTHUR: *Quakers in Science and Industry: Being an Account of the Quaker Contributions to Science and Industry During the 17th and 18th Centuries.* Bannisdale Press, London, 1950.

REID, JOHN: *The Scots Gard'ner.* Mainstream, Edinburgh, 1683.

SWEM, EARL GREGG (ed.): *Brothers of the Spade: Correspondence of Peter Collinson, of London, and of John Custis, of Williamsburg, Virginia, 1734-1746.* Proceedings of the American Antiquarian Society, London, 1948.

WAKEFIELD, PRISCILLA: *An Introduction to Botany, in a Series of Familiar Letters, with Illustrative Engravings.* Messrs P. Wogan, P. Byrne, Dublin, 1796

WHITE, GILBERT: *The Natural History of Selborne.* London, 1788-89.

WHITTAKER, E. JEAN: *Thomas Lawson 1630–1691: North Country Botanist, Quaker and Schoolmaster.* Sessions of York, 1986.

WHITTLE, TYLER and COOK, CHRISTOPHER: *Curtis's Flower Garden Displayed. 120 Plates from the Years 1787-1807.* Oxford University Press, Oxford, 1978, 1981.

WILLSON, E. J.: *James Lee and the Vineyard Nursery Hammersmith.* Hammersmith Local History Group, London, 1961

WOODVILLE, WILLIAM: *Medical Botany, Containing Systematic and General Descriptions, with Plates, of all the Medicinal Plants, Indigenous and Exotic, Comprehended in the Catalogues of the Materia Medica, as Published by the Royal Colleges of Physicians of London and Edinburgh: Accompanied with a Circumstantial Detail of their Medicinal Effects, and of the Diseases in which They Have Been Most Successfully Employed.* John Bohn, London, 1832.